THE MICROSCOPE
and
ITS USE

By

Frank J. Muñoz

TECHNICAL MICROSCOPE CONSULTANT

In Collaboration With

Dr. Harry A. Charipper

PROF. OF BIOLOGY, NEW YORK UNIVERSITY

1943

CHEMICAL PUBLISHING CO., INC.

BROOKLYN, N. Y.   U. S. A.

PREFACE

EARLY in 1942 a small, practical book on the microscope and its use was published in Spanish.* This
little book of 148 pages, including the glossary and
bibliography, was written for the Latin American scientists and students by one of the co-authors of this volume. Several North American scientists and professors
who had the opportunity to read it expressed the wish
that there were a similar book in English. It seems that
the pamphlets on the subject published by the manufacturers of microscopes are not sufficiently complete while
the large textbooks give far more than is necessary for
the average user of the microscope. Hence, there appears to be a definite need for a small, practical guide
to the use of this fascinating instrument, which we call
"the microscope."

Such a guide should be written, we were told, in very
clear, non-technical language and with suitable illustrations and diagrams where necessary. It should be
inexpensive so that any student or technician could
afford to buy it. All exhaustive and complete discus-
sions of "optics" should be eliminated, as they are readily
available, to those interested, in the more complete text-

---

* El Microscopio y su Uso. F. J. Muñoz. Editorial Tecnica Unida,
234 King St., Brooklyn, N. Y.

iii

books on the microscope or physics. However, the real practical everyday problems on the microscope and its use should be carefully explained and answered. We refer to questions such as: "I have a fluorite oil immersion lens; should I use it with a huyghenian or a compensating ocular?" or, "All the optical system of my microscope is, I know, perfect. It is clean and my slide well mounted and prepared, yet I cannot see some of its fine minute details as well as they appear on photomicrographs shown in my text book—WHY? What should I do so that I can see them as well or better?

We were also told that actual examples of the use of the microscope should be incorporated, not only for the biological sciences, but also for metallurgy, geology, ballistics, etc. Also the practical use and application of accessories should be mentioned and explained. There should be a comprehensive glossary covering definitions of words and terms commonly used in relation to the microscope. Also the table of contents for each chapter, as well as the index, should be quite complete.

Obviously, to write such a book two different types of authoritative experience are necessary. The experience of an educator who has taught thousands of students in a subject which requires the use of the microscope and that of an optical man who has had to meet and help to solve many and diverse problems in the use of the microscope as an instrument for research and teaching.

This book is not intended as a scientific treatise but as a guide to aid technicians and students in the use of the instrument. The material contained in the present volume is drafted from the authors' personal experience and from the sources to which acknowledgment is given, however, the authors assume full responsibility for the statements made and accuracy of the manuscript.

It is the sincere hope of the authors of this little volume that their contribution will satisfy the apparent need for a book to the above mentioned "specifications."

H. A. C.

F. J. M.

ACKNOWLEDGMENT

In PRESENTING this book the authors acknowledge very gratefully the help and cooperation of four microscope manufacturers and of several individuals.

Spencer Lens Company, of Buffalo, N. Y., Bausch & Lomb Optical Company, of Rochester, N. Y. and the New York Offices of E. Leitz, Inc. and Carl Zeiss, all very kindly furnished our publishers with the expensive cuts necessary to illustrate this book. Without this cooperation a book of this type would be considerably more expensive and perhaps beyond the reach of many people to whom we hope it will be of the greatest help.

Considerable assistance was obtained in the preparation of the manuscript from the various publications of Spencer Lens Company. Mr. R. Tvestmann furnished considerable interesting information included in Chapter IV.

Mr. Burton Dezendorf, of Spencer Lens Company, made available a great deal of the material used in the first chapter. Dr. K. Bauer, of Zeiss, and Mr. H. W. Zieler, of Leitz, supplied us with factual information regarding the histories of their Companies which is also included in the first chapter. Mr. I. L. Nixon, of Bausch & Lomb, was kind enough to supply some necessary information. Mr. William F. Butler, (of the Philadelphia Office of Spencer Lens Company) an expert on the use of polarizing microscopes contributed greatly to the content and structure of Chapter VIII.

To all the above mentioned Companies and persons, as well as to many others who helped and encouraged us in preparing this book, we express our most sincere thanks and appreciation.

THE AUTHORS

CONTENTS

Contents

Chapter I

THE EVOLUTION OF THE MICROSCOPE

THERE are indeed very few products in general use today which have as long and interesting a history as the microscope. Was it invented by anybody?—Or was it rather developed by a process of evolution?

There are available so many contradictory statements regarding this subject that it is difficult to state with authority that any one person invented this fascinating instrument. We know that Sir John Layard discovered a plano-convex lens of rock-crystal during his excavations at Nineveh. This would indicate that it was made around 721 to 705 B.C. Lucius Anneus Seneca, the Roman philosopher who died in 65 A.D. spoke of a glass globule filled with water which "will aid in seeing those difficult things that frequently escape the eye."

Undoubtedly the word lens is derived from the word "lenticula"—lentil—a bean-like vegetable with seeds shaped like a double convex lens. Thus, some of these early scientists and philosophers like Pliny, the Elder, who died in 79 A.D. spoke of "the burning property of *lenses* made of glass," and it is said that Nero used an

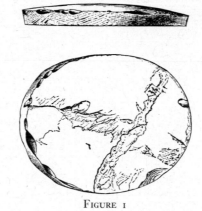

FIGURE 1

Rock Crystal discovered by Sir John Layard.

emerald as an *eye lens* when watching the gladiators at the Roman Amphitheater.

Robert Hooke speaks of a Dr. Francis Redi who stated that "bi-convex lenses" were in use in ancient Rome, but nevertheless we are not at all certain that any important development in optics came from the Rome of the Caesars. It is also said that the ancient Chinese wore spectacles and that they were fairly well versed in the science of optics long before our occidental world. However, this is probably untrue for some of their so-called "spectacles" which have come down to us were made of quartz and had plane surfaces. Thus, they could not be truly lenses and were more probably used as ornaments.

Some Italian writers claim that the inventor of spectacles was Salvino D'Armato of Florence, but the English believe that he got the idea from Roger Bacon who lived 50 years before. D'Armato's tomb, in the church of Santa Maria Maggiore, bears the following inscription: "Here lies Salvino D'Armato of the Amati of

Florence, Inventor of Spectacles, May the Lord forgive him his sins A.D. 1317."

In 1542 we find the first reference to the forerunner of the compound microscope, the "telescope." Nicholas Copernicus of Poland, using a crude instrument of his own making, observed the stars and planets in the skies and discovered that the sun rather than the earth was the center of our universe—that there were universes other than our own.

16th and 17th Centuries

Inspiration, ideas, enthusiasm and persistence seemed to motivate the early pioneers in the development of the microscope. These men may have realized the tremendous progress that the microscope would make possible. We know they were thrilled by the world of "the small" whose doors they were beginning to open, for we have read the exciting descriptions of what they saw, and have seen the queer drawings of their observations.

The magnifier or simple microscope must have been available as soon as eyeglass lenses. The compound microscope was apparently first mentioned in 1590. Zaccharias Janssen of Middleburg, Holland while experimenting with a telescope, found that elongating the tube of his instrument greatly enlarged near objects. This gave him the idea for his compound microscope which had an objective lens as well as an eyepiece. This invention ushered in a 200 year period of experimentation, invention and ecstatic exploration by a few men who had the time and desire to play with this complex toy.

Galileo made a similar instrument and improved Janssen's invention by mounting the tube so that it could be focused. He announced the invention of his microscope in 1610. Cornelius Drebbell of Belgium designed a microscope having a lens mounted in a brass cup, pro-

FIGURE 2

The microscope designed by Galileo in 1610.

vided with a brass strip on which to place the specimen, and a slit for the entry of light. Johannes Kepler, the German astronomer, who wrote "Kepler's Laws" relative to the motion of planets, also made a microscope of the Janssen type. He used convex lenses throughout, and obtained an inverted image of the object under observation.

Campini's discovery that lenses could be ground was an outstanding contribution. Previously lenses had been formed on the ends of glass rods, by heating, but obviously it was practically impossible to reproduce any given spherical lens curvature. Campini's discovery therefore was an important turning point in the science of optics.

Now we come to Anthony Van Leeuwenhoek who was one of the first men to *seriously* study objects with the microscope. To him the microscope was more than a clever toy to play with and amuse his friends. To him it was a means to an end, the tool that would allow him to explore an unknown world. He observed and wrote

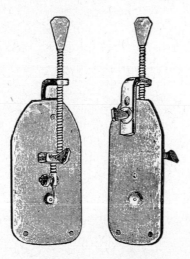

FIGURE 3

A Van Leeuwenhoek microscope.

on a countless number of things, vegetable mold, the perfection of the stinger of a flea, the foot of a fly, and the faceted eye of an insect. Just before he died in 1723 he discovered the existence of tiny organisms in water and in the saliva of the mouth and wrote excitedly of his "wrigglers" and "worms" as he called them. His second discovery was the existence of corpuscles in the blood. He observed the red corpuscles and was able to identify them as such and to properly describe them. Undoubtedly these discoveries of Van Leeuwenhoek were the foundation of the structure of modern medicine, for they pointed the way to the later researches of men like Pasteur and Koch.

His microscopes were not compound microscopes, they were simple microscopes consisting of a single lens, very small, of about ⅛th of an inch in diameter and having a strong curve to produce a fairly high magnification. They had an ingenious device to bring the object very close to the lens for proper observation. They must have been difficult and awkward to use, but nevertheless many momentous discoveries were made with them.

Robert Hooke, of England, member of the Royal Microscopical Society, published his "Micrographia" describing tissue structure, blood vessel sections and many other objects and forms. He later used the doublet telescope eyepiece of Christian Huyghens, a Dutch mathematician and physicist, to make a compound microscope out of his single lens. He was credited by

FIGURE 4

Microscope used by Robert Hooke in 1665.

the Royal Microscopical Society as being the inventor of the true compound microscope.

It is interesting to find that, even at such an early period, the use of two eyes in observations with a microscope was being considered. In Orleans two matched Keplerian microscopes were used so mounted that they converged from the eyes of the worker to the point of focus. Obviously this was the forerunner of the stereoscopic microscopes of later years.

18th Century

During this period the fundamental physical structure of the latter day instruments was worked out and the foundations were laid for the fine lens work which was done in the following years.

Mr. Stephen Gray, in England, developed what he called "the water microscope." It was like Van Leeuwenhoek's, but used a drop of water in a ring instead of a glass lens. The curved surface of the water gave the magnification.

FIGURE 5

Adams Microscope with revolving objective holder.

During the first half of the century, three men, Wilson, Marshall and Adams, experimented with the possibilities of lenses made of various varnishes instead of glass, but each of them in turn concluded that there was no possibility of using these materials successfully because they oxidized so rapidly.

A very important discovery of this period was that of John Dolland in England when he made an achromatic lens, a lens with certain color corrections. This brought forth tremendous possibilities for the future manufacture of lenses. He experimented with combinations of "hard" and "soft" glass.

Andrew Pritchard, also in England, observed birefringence with natural mineral crystals. He later made lenses of rubies, sapphires, garnets and other gem stones, but was unable, because of the color of these stones to use them successfully in a lens system, and gave up his experiments disheartened.

FIGURE 6
Nachet binocular microscope.

Dr. David Brewster, of the Royal Microscopical Society, also worked with natural mineral crystals. He felt that the higher refrangibility of these natural crystals should permit grinding lenses of longer radii and still produce magnifications as high as those obtained with glass lenses. He also experimented with immersing of object and lens. Some of the work of these men was carried out during the beginning of the 19th century.

In this same period in Italy, Dr. Giovanni Batista Amici, of the University of Modena, failing to make an achromatic microscope objective, turned his attention to a reflecting microscope, erecting the image by means of a prism and allowing the object to lie on the glass table of his instrument. This leads us to the constructive era of the 19th Century.

19th Century

At the beginning of the 19th Century the basic form of the microscope, as we know it today, had been established. Men no longer looked upon the Van Leeuwenhoek single lens instrument as the "most practical." The compound microscope offered greater convenience and adaptability to the many problems investigated by men of this period. The stage was set for a period of rapid development.

The acceptance of the microscope by scientists of this period was an encouragement to the builders, who in turn stimulated more active use of the instrument by a continuous succession of improvements and inventions. Among the early users in America was the naturalist, Washington Irving, and Dr. J. W. Bailey at West Point. In Europe, Schleiden and Schwann used microscopes in discovering the multi-cellular structure of organisms. Audouin discovered that the disease, Muscardini, of the silkworms, was really a fungus vegetation growing within their bodies. Three French-

FIGURE 7

Chevalier achromatic microscope.

men, Thuret, Talsane and Decaisne, used polarized light in the examination of ferns, fungi and marine algae. Naegeli of Naples, probably the first true cytologist was working during the middle of the century, as was Charles Darwin, who wrote "The Origin of Species" in 1859, basing much of his work on observations through the microscope. Many other scientists were using the microscope, all were suggesting improvements aiding in the evolution of the instrument.

Swift development brought the first use of the Ramsden, or positive eyepiece, blueglass (daylight) discs, bull's eye condensers below the stage, achromatic condensers, binocular bodies, revolving nosepieces, par-

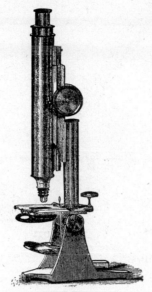

FIGURE 8

Smith & Beck student microscope

focal mounting of objectives, graduated mechanical stages, polarizing accessories on rotating stage research microscopes, iris diaphragms, lever type side fine adjustments, special rotating stages and oblique light accessories.

In Germany, Joseph Fraunhofer, physicist, after mapping the bands of the spectrum, constructed an achromatic microscope objective, reported the first to be made, though his contribution was never credited with being of value. His work was followed by M. Sellignes, whose first successful achromatic microscope objective stirred considerable interest, especially on the part of Professor Amici, who had failed before. Amici, returning to the problem, constructed his objective with three sets of lenses which could be adjusted so as

FIGURE 9
Ross large compound microscope.

to correct errors. This became a standard practice in lens making, followed for many years.

Tulley, of London, working at the suggestion of a member of the Royal Microscopical Society, and reputedly without the knowledge of the success of Sellignes, produced an achromatic triplet, that, while of very low power, was stated to have been better corrected than any brought to the Royal Microscopical Society before that time. J. J. Lister, also working on the achromatic objective, found means of making additional corrections. In 1837, Andrew Ross of England, discovered the principle of cover glass correction and manufactured objectives with correction collars. Rev. J. B. Reade, also of England, constructed a true dark field illuminator. In France, Nachet designed the first mechanical stage. Both Nachet and Dujardin worked on the problem of illumination developing substage condensers. Nachet produced a binocular microscope having one objective by using a prism to divide the light, much as is done today.

Dr. William Clyde Wollaston and Henry Coddington, both of the Royal Microscopical Society, devised magnifiers which were later used by John Quekett in his dissecting microscope. Instruments of this type are still used.

During this period, competition was keen to see who could make objectives with the best correction and the highest power. Achromatic objectives were made 1/50, 1/75 and 1/100 of an inch in focal length. The results of the efforts of these workers were never kept secret but were published immediately for the benefit of all.

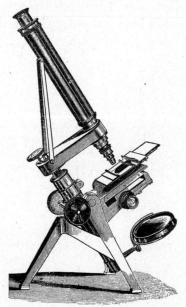

FIGURE 10

Powell & Leland large compound microscope.

The Advent of Microscope Manufacturers and Some of Their Contributions

Early Scientists and teachers—men who were not interested in constructing microscopes but needed instruments in their search for knowledge—called upon the advanced amateurs of the day, asking for assistance. They offered financial inducements to those who would construct microscopes for them. Some of the important manufacturing companies were founded in this manner.

History indicates that the first man to start the manufacture of microscopes for others, was Dr. C. L. Chevalier, of France, who, in 1825, constructed his first microscope objective and presented it to the Royal Society, in England, of which he, as a physician, was an honorary member. He received so much encouragement from the Society that he founded the firm of Chevalier and Son, in Paris. In England, Beck, a nephew of Lister, was so stimulated by the latter's enthusiasm, that he associated himself with James Smith, who at that time, was making microscope stands and objectives of good quality. From this association grew the firm of R. & J. Beck Company. In 1832, Leland joined with Powell and started the firm of Powell & Leland, for the manufacture of microscopes and they produced very fine instruments. In the same year, Andrew Ross started manufacturing achromatic objectives and stands. In 1845, Nachet, in France, started his long career, producing his first microscope.

Until 1838, the development work on microscopes had been done by Europeans. The first American who enters the picture is Charles A. Spencer, of Canastota, New York (1813–1881), who, as a boy, had an interest in lenses, constructed his own crude lathe and shaped an achromatic lens system of the telescope type—the first achromatic lens made in America.

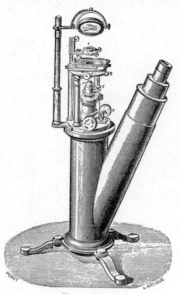

FIGURE 11

Nachet inverted microscope.

In 1847, Spencer visited his friend, Professor J. W. Bailey, of West Point, at which time he saw the microscope Chevalier had made for Dr. Gillman. Spencer, then nearing 40, declared that he had made better microscopes. Dr. Gillman immediately gave Spencer an order to produce a microscope; and Spencer, although he had declared that he would never work with his hands to make instruments for sale, returned to Canastota at the end of the visit, committed to the commercial production of a microscope. This first, commercially made, American microscope was delivered to Dr. Gillman in the early fall of 1847. The praise of both Dr. Gillman and Professor Bailey, so encouraged Spencer that he founded the firm of Charles A. Spencer and Sons Company. Only five microscopes were in use in the City of New York at this time.

In 1851, the American Association for the Advancement of Science, published in their "Proceedings," a committee report stating that Charles A. Spencer was making the best objective lenses in the world. Perhaps the Association was not too enthusiastic, since we find the same praise coming from Europe for the American made objectives. Comments from Amici, Carpenter, Tulley and Naegeli all expressed a high regard. Spencer, during this period, constructed lenses of fluorite, with corrections similar to those of present day apochromatic objectives, although they were not called apochromats. He experimented with calcite and quartz, as well as fluorite and concluded that fluorite was the material best adapted for use in objective lenses.

Three mechanical developments of this American manufacturer were the trunnion microscope, described by Carpenter as having "everything" in its construction, the inclination joint which Spencer and Chevalier had pioneered, but which was not taken up by the other manufacturers until about 1854, and the lever type side fine adjustment mechanism. Later Spencer Lens Company developed the combination monocular and binocular body, the variable inclination binocular body and other practical improvements. The independence of the feeding mechanism from the object clamp in rotary microtomes (a real improvement) was also developed by Spencer.

Associated with the Spencer name in the manufacture of microscopes at different periods, were Messers. May,

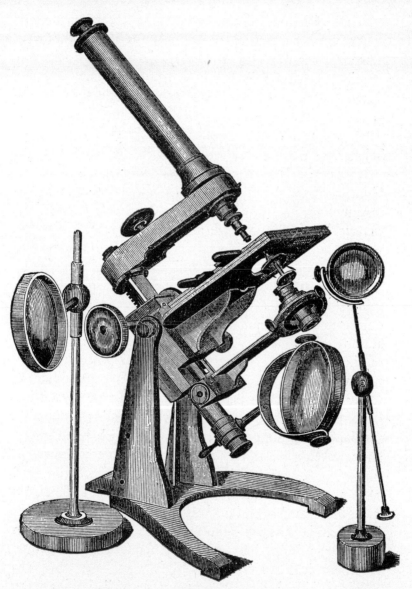

FIGURE 12

The Spencer Trunnion microscope.

17

Eaton, Smith and Tolles. Paul and H. R. Spencer were sons of the founder. H. R. Spencer carried on the business after the death of his father, moving to Buffalo in 1891 and changing the name of the firm in 1895 to Spencer Lens Company. Recently Spencer Lens Company became affiliated with the American Optical Company of Southbridge, Massachusetts, and it is now the Scientific Instrument Division of that organization.

Robert B. Tolles, a youthful spectacle maker of Geneva, New York entered the field of microscope manufacture in the earliest days, became interested in the work of Spencer and, after working with him for 15 years went into business for himself, gaining considerable fame for his excellent objectives. Tolles concentrated his attention on the work of Spencer in natural minerals and produced fluorite objectives of very fine correction, publishing his computations in the transactions of the Royal Microscopical Society. He read of the accounts of Brewster, who held objects in contact with his lenses by water, and after considerable study of effective aperture, constructed true immersion objectives. Water and balsam were used as immersion media. He indulged in an argument with the English amateur, Wenham, over the value of wide apertures in objectives and the ultimate angles possible. Not until 1885 was the argument settled in favor of Tolles. His 1/18 inch immersion lens was then considered the finest in England. The computation of his fluorite immersion lens was published by both the American and Royal Microscopical Societies.

The J. W. Queen & Company, of Philadelphia were producing complete microscopes about 1896. Joseph Zentmayer of the same city offered creditable stands in 1877.

Edward Bausch made his first microscope in 1872 and exhibited at the Philadelphia Centennial in 1876. The son of J. J. Bausch, founder of the Bausch & Lomb Optical Company, of Rochester, New York, he had available the facilities of an already large optical manufacturing plant. He worked with the microscopists of his day—the doctors, educators, men who were forming study groups and microscopical societies. He studied their needs, constructed instruments of suitable design, then instructed his associates in the most efficient methods of production. He was the first man to organize production of microscopes in quantity. The fine quality of the resulting product won world wide recognition. Since then Bausch & Lomb has made many practical contributions. As far as we know they were the first to manufacture the "reversed type" microscope and the "drum" nosepiece for stereoscopic microscopes.

In Europe, Ernst Leitz purchased the Kellner Optical Works in 1865. This was the beginning of the Leitz Works.

About 1870 Leitz produced research microscopes for the Biological Sciences, and since then the Leitz contributions have been numerous and helpful. Outstanding among them are those by their brilliant scientist Dr. M. Berek. He gave theoretical as well as practical proof of the fact that the resolving power in dark field is equal to that in bright field at identical numerical apertures of observation. This new theory released a spontaneous development of dark field condensers with high numerical apertures. It also led to the development of dark field illuminators for reflected light such as the "Ultropak." Other important contributions by Berek are to be found in the development of the science of ore microscopy in reflected polarized light.

Until 1925, the production of E. Leitz covered almost exclusively the many fields of microscopy. In 1925 the Leica camera (the first precision miniature camera) appeared and pioneered an entirely new field in photography. Since then, many accessories have been created for the Leica camera adapting it to microscopic work and thus it became a valuable tool to record microscopic observations.

The Micro-Summars for macrophotography (1896), the bispherical dark field condensers (1907), periplane eyepieces (1914) and the Berek compensator for polarizing microscopes, are other Leitz contributions to the microscope field.

In England in 1875 another firm whose products are distributed throughout the world entered the field, William Watson and Sons Company of London. They make good optics and precision optical instruments.

The firm of Carl Zeiss, Jena, was founded in 1846 and for about fifty years, microscopes were the principal products.

In 1866 Professor Abbe, of the University of Jena, became associated with Zeiss. He applied himself to the theories of Scientific lens design. His "Theory of Microscope Image Formation," has shown the importance of considering diffraction effects in the use of the microscope. A contribution of great importance was his application of the sine condition to optical design which made the mathematical calculation of lenses possible. He invented the Abbe substage condenser.

In 1878 Abbe, *who by that time had become a partner of Carl Zeiss*, developed the homogeneous oil immersion lens, and in 1886 the apochromatic objective.

At the same time that Abbe was formulating the theoretical and mathematical aspects of optics, and Carl Zeiss was putting optical theory into practice, Dr. Schott and Abbe were working on the creation of the new Jena optical glass. These three men were drawn together by their common interest and cooperated with each other in connection with formulae, glass of the required optical characteristics, and excellent manufacturing facilities. Their systematic methods and outstanding abilities contributed greatly, not only to the optical industry, but to science and industry generally.

Since then Zeiss has made many other contributions in the field of microscopes and precision optics.

20th Century

Until the beginning of the 20th century, the manufacture of microscopes was the work of individual craftsmen—men who could make complete instruments. The metal work was done by hand, lens grinding and polishing were done on crude equipment. Instruments were assembled one at a time. Most of the manufacturers had work shops consisting of two or three rooms. The few microscopes possessed by the colleges were used only for demonstration. Only a scattering of physicians and scientists were demanding instruments.

Rapid change marked the first years of the 20th century. The work of Pasteur, Lister, Koch and others had startled the world. Young doctors were returning from Europe with a knowledge of the new science of bacteriology. Microscopes were now as essential in medicine as in botany and zoology. An insistent demand for microscopes began to tax the facilities of the manufacturers. Colleges, Physicians, Health Depart-

ments of cities and Hospitals sent in their requirements;
two, six, fifty instruments at a time. To meet the demand from all of these sources required a new order
of efficiency and better manufacturing facilities in the
production of microscopes. This brought the scientist
with his exact mathematical methods of computation,
the engineer with his standards and tolerances, the de-
signer with his knowledge of the scientific need for his
product, and the manufacturer with his ability for large
scale production—to handle the greatly increased demand for the microscope in science and industry.

Production methods were established in which spe-
cialization of workers, a new type of craftsmanship,
replaced the slow and tedious methods of old. Men
were trained in single tasks—lens surfacing, mounting
or assembling—and made it a life work, developing great
skill and speed while producing a uniform product.
Standards were set establishing uniform sizes to facili-
tate interchangeability of parts of instruments and accessories produced by the various manufacturers. Some
standards were adopted by all manufacturers, such as
the eyepiece diameter and the "Society" screw thread
on objectives. Tolerances—limits of accuracy between
which a measurement must come—were set by each
manufacturer establishing the optical and mechanical
quality of his product. The 20th century so far, has
been a period for the refinement of the product and
improvement of manufacturing facilities.

The application of the microscope has been extended
into almost every science and industry. To meet exactly
the special needs which have been developed in these
various fields, it has been necessary to construct many
strange variations of the standard microscope. Equip-

ments made up of cameras and microscopes; projectors and microscopes; machine tools and microscopes; stereoscopic; polarizing and metallurgical microscopes. It is now possible to acquire if one wishes a microscope properly designed to fit practically all known applications of this marvelous instrument.

The Electron Microscope *

It would not be proper to close this chapter without the statement of a few facts regarding *the latest* development in the microscope field "The Electron Microscope."

This instrument has been developed because optical microscopes apparently have just about reached the limit of resolution and magnification possible with *light*. Electronics, which are free of many of the limitations inherent in optical lenses and light, make it possible to go far beyond the optical microscope both in resolution and magnification.

The electron microscope uses the flow of electrons in a manner analogous to the use of light rays in the optical microscope. It controls the path of these electrons by means of axially symmetric electric or magnetic fields which act upon electrons as glass lenses act upon light. In other words, in the electron microscope we have basically the same system for the formation of an image as we have in the optical microscope: light source, condenser, object under observation, objective (which forms and magnifies the primary image) and the ocular projector lens. However, these parts instead of being glass lenses are magnetic fields and they can

* "An Electron Microscope for Practical Laboratory Service," V. K. Leworkin, J. Hillier, A. W. Vance, published by AIEE Committee and "Recent Developments in the Electron Microscope," James Hillier and A. W. Vance from Proceedings of the I. R. E. Vol. 29, No. 4.

also be focused and the magnification increased or decreased just like in the optical microscope.

This type of microscope naturally also has its limitations and problems. It is necessarily very expensive in comparison with the optical microscope; since air interferes with the flow of the eletrons, the entire electron optical path of the microscope must be under vacuum, and finally, the object under observation must be placed on a thin cellulose film of only about 0.000001 centimeter thick. The image is viewed on a fluorescent screen or it can be photographed and studied later. The fact remains, however, that regardless of these problems which are strange to the user of an optical microscope, it offers tremendous possibilities for the research of the future.

CHAPTER II

THE MODERN MICROSCOPE

BASICALLY there are two kinds of microscopes, the simple microscope and the compound microscope.

The Simple Microscope

The optics of a simple microscope consist of only one lens or of a combination of lenses mounted together in order to perform as one lens. Naturally if such a lens consists of more than one element it is usually better corrected for color and spherical aberrations, and offers greater possibilities for higher magnifications. The best lenses are those called "triplets" having three elements. These triplets have excellent corrections and usually give a larger field of view than the "doublet" lenses (which have only two elements) of a similar magnifying power. Also, the triplets have a longer working distance, that is they can be focused upon the object at a point farther away from it than the doublets. This is at times very helpful. Naturally, the triplets are more expensive than the doublets.

These lenses, either doublets or triplets are mounted on simple stands such as those illustrated in figures 14 and 15. When the stand is equipped with a rack and pinion

The Microscope

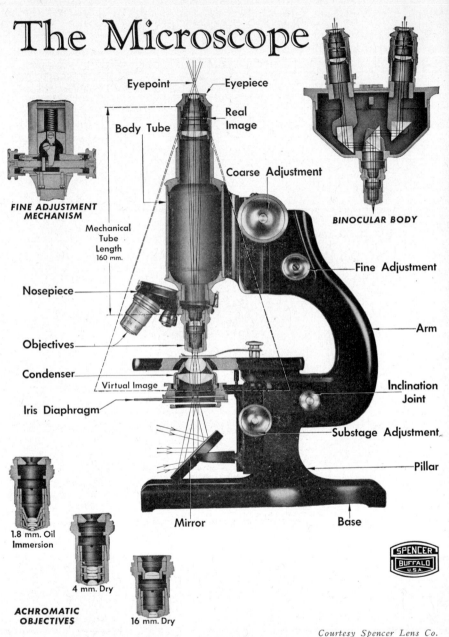

Eyepoint — Eyepiece

Body Tube

Real Image

Coarse Adjustment

FINE ADJUSTMENT MECHANISM

Mechanical Tube Length 160 mm.

BINOCULAR BODY

Fine Adjustment

Nosepiece

Arm

Objectives

Condenser

Virtual Image

Iris Diaphragm

Inclination Joint

Substage Adjustment

Pillar

1.8 mm. Oil Immersion

4 mm. Dry

16 mm. Dry

ACHROMATIC OBJECTIVES

Mirror

Base

FIGURE 13

The Compound Microscope, showing parts and the path of light through the instrument.

focusing adjustment it is possible to use magnifiers giving increases in size of as much as 24 diameters. On a simple microscope, however, high magnifications are not very practical, for in order to see properly the object under observation, one must put the eye very close to the lens and since its working distance is short, one's nose is entirely too close to the specimen when it is brought into focus. Usually, it is best to use these simple microscopes for magnifications of no more than 15x. The most practical lenses to use are those which give magnifications of 6, 9, or 12 diameters. Let us remember that:

Courtesy Spencer Lens Co.

FIGURE 14

A small dissecting microscope.

Courtesy Spencer Lens Co.

FIGURE 15

A dissecting microscope with hand rests and rack and pinion focusing adjustment.

a—The more magnification the smaller the field of view.

b—The higher the magnification the shorter the working distance of the lens.

c—The lenses of high magnification have less depth of focus than those of lower magnifying power.

d—When using a magnifier of 6x or more (we *do not* refer to a reading glass) either in the hand or when mounted on a microscope stand it is necessary to put the eye very close to the lens. If this is not done it is impossible to get the full field of view of which it is capable and the magnification obtained will not be that for which the lens is rated.

These simple microscopes give us an image which is right side up, that is, it is not inverted like in the compound microscopes. Hence they are sometimes called *dissecting microscopes* for they are very convenient for dissections in the laboratories when it is not necessary to use a magnification of more than 9 or 12x. When it is necessary to use higher magnifications for a dissection it is better to use a "stereoscopic" microscope which is discussed in Chapter VI.

The Compound Microscope

This type of microscope is well illustrated in figure 13. One can see at once that it is much more complicated, it has many more optical and mechanical parts. It is capable of giving us much higher magnifications but it gives a reversed image, that is, the object is seen upside down and wrong side to.* Let us study this

---

* The exception is the stereoscopic microscope wherein the image is erected by prisms.

instrument and see of what parts it consists and what function is performed by each one of its important parts. There are many variations of the compound microscope, the binocular microscope, the stereoscopic microscope, the metallurgical microscope, the polarizing microscope and even special stands for dark field illumination only; however, all of these variations which it has been necessary to develop to meet special needs

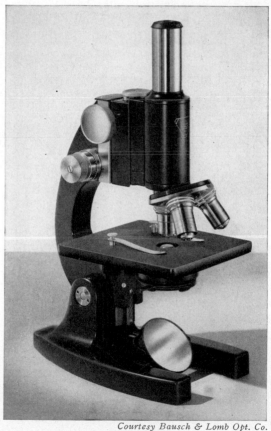

Courtesy Bausch & Lomb Opt. Co.

FIGURE 16

A modern medical microscope.

have their optical principles based on the conventional microscope. It is necessary therefore to study this well before one can understand a more specialized type. In the chapters that follow we shall study the specialized microscopes.

The Optical Train

We note that its optical parts consist of:

a—*The Mirror.* This is the part which first receives the light whether it is daylight coming from a window or artificial light from a lamp. It usually has two reflecting surfaces, one on each side, one plane and the other concave. One should always use *the plane* surface if the microscope is equipped with a condenser. The only exception to this should be when the mirror reflects over the image of the object a secondary image, for example, branches and leaves from a tree near a window. In such a case it may be necessary to use the concave surface of the mirror but the results will not be quite as perfect with the higher powers. If the microscope *is not* equipped with a condenser the concave surface is used because it acts as a substitute for the condenser although not as effective.

b—*The Condenser.* Its purpose is to concentrate the light coming from the mirror to a point approximately 1.25 mm above the surface of its top lens, which is the place where the object will be located, since microscope slides are usually between 1 mm and 1.25 mm thick. The condenser is equipped with an iris diaphragm which controls the amount of light it will deliver, and the angle at which the light rays emerge to the optical axis. It should be remembered that if the iris diaphragm of the condenser is closed beyond a certain point and if

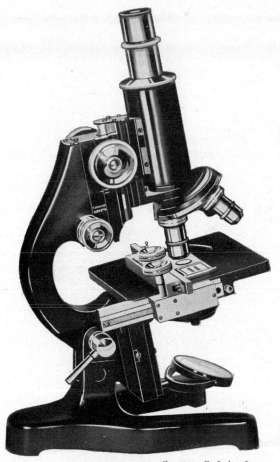

Courtesy E. Leitz, Inc.

FIGURE 17

Medical microscope with attached ungraduated mechanical stage.

this point does not allow the light rays to emerge at a sufficiently wide angle, it will not be possible to get the full efficiency of the objective lens of the microscope, i.e., the lens will not render its full numerical aperture. This means that its ability to resolve an object into its component parts will be reduced. Modern

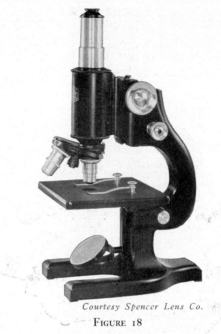

Courtesy Spencer Lens Co.

FIGURE 18

High school microscope without condenser.

microscope condensers are marked with the numerical aperture which they will render at various points of the opening of the iris diaphragm. Therefore, it is very easy to check this and guard against closing the iris to a point which will reduce the rated numerical aperture of the objective being used at the time. If the light is too strong at the correct opening of the iris for the objective in use, then the strength of the source of light should be reduced or neutral tint filters (which reduce the amount of transmitted light) should be placed between the illuminant and the mirror. It is perfectly permissible and usual to reduce the light by means of the iris diaphragm if it is not necessary to obtain the *maximum* numerical aperture of the objective in use.

Since not all microscope slides are of exactly the same thickness the condenser is mounted in such a way as to be movable up and down. Thus it is possible to focus it to the exact point where it will render optimum results. The better the optical corrections of the condenser, the more carefully it should be focused and centered, therefore many of the large research micro-

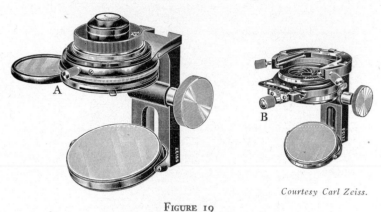

Courtesy Carl Zeiss.

FIGURE 19

Substage—Abbe illuminating apparatus. (A)—with sliding sleeve condenser. (B)—with centering slide.

Courtesy Spencer Lens Co.

FIGURE 20

Fork type substage.

scopes which are equipped with highly corrected achromatic and aplanatic condensers, having as many as six
elements, have a fine adjustment for focusing the condenser in addition to the usual rack and pinion, also
the necessary centering screws.

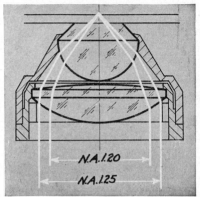

Courtesy Spencer Lens Co.

FIGURE 21

Path of light through the condenser.

Double   Triple   Quadruple

Courtesy E. Leitz, Inc.

FIGURE 22

Revolving nosepieces.

A standard Abbe condenser such as shown in figure
21 consisting of only two elements does not require
very careful focusing. Generally it can be used effectively at its highest position determined by the manufacturer, and lowered a bit if exceptionally thin

slides are used. It must be remembered however that if the condenser is not in its approximate correct position in relation to the object the light will be reduced and it is impossible to obtain even passable results with a high power oil immersion objective.

The mirror and the condenser with its focusing mechanism are called *the substage* of the microscope because they are under the stage of the instrument.

c—The Objectives. They are called objective lenses because they are immediately above the object under observation. They are the most important lenses of the microscope. It is their mission to form and magnify the image of the object. They are often mounted on a *revolving nosepiece* rather than on the tube itself so that two, three or four objectives will be ready for instant use. These revolving nosepieces, figure 22, make it possible to rotate the desired objective into its working position without the necessity of unscrewing one objective from the tube of the microscope and screwing the next one into the same position.

Modern objectives are usually marked with their magnifying power and their rated Numerical Aperture. For example, 10x—N.A.—0.25 means that a lens so marked will give a magnification of ten *diameters* and that the highest numerical aperture it can render is 0.25. At this writing the two American manufacturers, Spencer and Bausch and Lomb, also mark their objectives with their equivalent focus. That is "the focus of a single theoretical lens which has the same power and the same characteristics than the combination of lenses composing the lens considered." This *must not* be confused with the *working distance* of the objective which is usually different than its marked focus.

If an objective is marked 16 mm it does not mean that it will be in focus 16 mm away from the object. There are various factors which affect the working distance of an objective such as the length of the tube which is being used, what ocular is in place at the top of the tube, whether the worker is short or far sighted, etc. In other words, the working distance of an objective is variable to a certain extent depending upon the person who uses it and in what way it is being used. The equivalent focus is not variable.

If the magnification of the objective is multiplied by the magnification of the ocular being used with it, the product will be the total magnification of the combination at the eye point. This is also about the same magnification which will be obtained on a photographic plate or a screen ten inches away from the ocular. If an image is projected on to a screen or photographic plate with the same combination of lenses a longer distance than ten inches, the magnification obtained will increase proportionally. If it is projected less than ten inches, it will decrease in the same manner.

Usually the higher the magnification of the objective the less is its working distance and the higher its numerical aperture. Also generally, the larger the number of lens elements necessary to form the complete objective. If we refer again to figure 13 we see that the 16 mm achromatic objective shown therein has 4 lenses, the 4 mm has 5 and the 1.8 mm which is an oil immersion objective (with a magnifying power of 95x) has 6 lenses. Not only do objectives vary as to their focus, magnifying power and numerical aperture, they also differ in their color corrections. There are the achromatic objectives which are corrected for two colors of the spectrum and spherically for one. These are the lenses which are most commonly used because their cost is not too high and their results perfectly adequate for most routine work. There are the apochromatic objectives which are corrected for three colors of the spectrum and spherically for two. These objectives are much more expensive because they are composed of more lens elements, are manufactured in smaller quantities and are very difficult to construct. Their numerical aperture is generally higher than that of achromatic objectives of similar focus and magnification. There are also the semi-apochromats whose color correction is better than that of the achromats but not as good as of the apochromats. These lenses are often called fluorite objectives because fluorite crystals are used in their construction. One also finds the quartz lenses which are used for photomicrography with ultraviolet light.

The apochromatic objectives are generally used for difficult research work where it is necessary to obtain the very best resolution of an object with a minimum of color defects and very especially for photomicrography.

The fluorite objectives (or semi-apochromats) are particularly useful to bacteriologists who wish a better color correction than that obtained with the achromats but do not need the perfection of the "apos" (apochromats). They are better than the achromats for photomicrography.

The achromatic objectives are used with huyghenian or wide field oculars. The performance of the higher power dry objectives can sometimes be improved somewhat by the use of the hyperplane or of the compensating oculars or their equivalent.* The *ideal* oculars to use with the oil immersion achromats are the compensat-

* Hyperplane is a Bausch & Lomb trade term.

ing.** *The above does not mean however that it is necessary to use oculars other than the standard huyghenian to get good results with these objectives.* As a matter of fact for the majority of routine work the huyghenian oculars are used exclusively in most laboratories.

The same holds true for the fluorites except that the improvement when using with them hyperplane or compensating oculars is slightly more apparent.

The apochromatic objectives should always be used with compensating oculars. The only exception is that in photomicrography it is sometimes advisable to use the special projection eyepieces designed for them. It is also better to use the same make of compensating ocular with the same make of apochromatic objective. For example, with a Zeiss apochromat always use a Zeiss compensating ocular, with a Spencer apochromat, a Spencer compensating ocular, etc. This is due to the fact that there seems to be a greater variation in the formulae used by the various manufacturers in the construction of these optics than there is in the manufacture of the less complicated lenses. This is not generally necessary with the achromats and fluorites, with them one can use combinations of oculars and objectives of different manufacture with perfectly satisfactory results.

The following table published in one of the Bausch & Lomb catalogs and included here with their permission may be of some help. By following this table one may obtain the clearest image possible with B. & L. optics provided all other relevant factors are properly controlled. Although this table is a good guide it does

** The Leitz Company calls its compensating oculars "Periplans."

not necessarily mean that the combinations will be as effective with optics other than B. & L.

E.F. mm means Equivalent Focus in millimeters.

Objective Used	E.F. mm	Most Satisfactory Eyepiece
Achromatic	48.0	Huyghenian
Achromatic	40.0	Huyghenian
Achromatic	32.0	Huyghenian
Achromatic	16.0	Huyghenian
Achromatic	8.0	Hyperplane
Achromatic	7.0	Hyperplane
Achromatic	4.0	Hyperplane
Achromatic	3.0	Hyperplane
Achromatic	1.9*	Compensating
Fluorite	4.0	Hyperplane
Fluorite	1.8*	Hyperplane
Fluorite	1.8*	Compensating
Apochromatic	16.0	Compensating
Apochromatic	8.0	Compensating
Apochromatic	4.0	Compensating
Apochromatic	3.0	Compensating
Apochromatic	2.0*	Compensating
Apochromatic	1.5*	Compensating

d—*The Oculars or Eyepieces.* These lenses are placed into the top of the tube of the microscope. Their function is to magnify still more the image formed by the objective lens and to project this image. The position of the eye point of the oculars varies, some have it higher than others depending on their design. By placing one's eye exactly at the right eye point one can see the full image formed by the microscope. Unless the oculars are of the "high eye point type" their eye point is usually three or four millimeters (sometimes less) above the upper surface of their top lens. This is the reason why a person wearing spectacles as he uses

* Oil Immersion Objective.

the microscope cannot see as wide a field as he would if he were not wearing glasses.

There are various types of oculars. The huyghenian, which cannot be used as hand magnifiers unless they are turned upside down, they have the diaphragm between the lenses; the Ramsden, which can be used as hand magnifiers and have the diaphragm below the lenses; the wide field, popular among pathologists; the high eye point, which are useful for people who must wear glasses while working with the microscope; the hyperplane type for flatter field images; the compensating, generally used with apochromatic objectives; and finally those specially designed for photomicrography or projection only, which cannot be properly used for visual work. Often their names tell us for what use they have been designed and we have given some practical information about this question in the discussion relating to the objectives.

To summarize, we have seen that the optical train of a microscope consists of:

> a—the mirror
> b—the condenser
> c—the objective
> d—the ocular

This optical train is of course, the "heart" of the microscope. The most beautiful and complete stand without a good optical train would be quite useless. At the same time however, the stand must be practical and so well constructed that it will permit us to obtain the best possible results from the optics of our microscope.

The Stand

The stand of the microscope is so designed that it will hold securely the various optical parts in perfect alignment. Also, it is provided with the necessary focusing adjustments. Let us study its various parts.

We see (fig. 13) that it has a heavy "horse shoe base." Then we come to the focusing mechanism for the condenser which may be a rack and pinion or, in older microscopes, the so-called "quick screw" mounting. The rack and pinion type supports the condenser more securely and holds it in more perfect alignment at its various possible positions, therefore practically all the well known manufacturers have discarded the "quick screw" in favor of the rack and pinion.* Going still higher we find the "stage" so called because the object is placed thereon for our examination. The stage may be plain or equipped with mechanical movements which permit us to move the object from side to side and forward and back.** Now we find the "tube" which has the objectives attached to one end by means of the nose-piece and receives the oculars at the other.

The tube of the microscope has a length predetermined by the manufacturer. This mechanical tube length is important due to the fact that the objectives are calculated for use with a certain length of tube. Let us remember that in modern microscopes the words "tube length" refer to the distance between the lower surface of the rotating part of the nosepiece and the top of the tube. It *does not* refer to the tube only minus the nosepiece. If our modern microscope is not

* This focusing mechanism is sometimes also referred to as "the sub-stage."
** See mechanical Stages, Chapter IX.

equipped with a nosepiece it should have a so called "single nosepiece adapter" which together with the tube itself gives us the correct tube length. Microscopes made by Spencer, Bausch & Lomb, Zeiss and Reichert have a standard tube length of 160 mm. Those of Leitz 170 mm.

As we said before although it is true that, *all other things being equal*, an objective designed for use with a tube length of 160 mm will give better results on a tube having such a dimension than if it is used with a tube 170 mm long, nevertheless, there are so many other factors to be considered that we feel this point may have been somewhat overemphasized by the majority of persons who have written about the microscope. Since objectives are not only designed for a certain tube length but also for a definite cover glass thickness it follows that if we use the wrong thickness of cover glass we would have to change the length of the tube. If the cover glass is too thick we must shorten the length of the tube, if it is too thin we must elongate it. Actually this question of cover glass thickness used is *more important* than the tube length, for each .01 mm difference in the ideal thickness of a cover glass requires a change of tube length of about 10 mm. We do not hesitate to state that for all practical purposes it is perfectly satisfactory to use for instance a Leitz objective (for a 170 mm tube length) on a Spencer microscope which has a tube 160 mm long. The ideal of course, is the right tube length with the right cover glass thickness.*

For the above reason some microscopes are equipped with tubes which can be shortened and lengthened

* The usual correction for cover glass thickness is for 0.17 or 0.18 mm.

within certain limits; in other words, they have a "draw tube." This is fine for a careful microscopist who checks with extreme care every factor affecting the use of his microscope, but where various people use the same microscope the draw tube may be more of a disadvantage than an asset. For example, since the objectives are parfocal (when one changes from one to the other the next one will require very slight focusing if the previous one used was perfectly focused) *only* at the correct tube length, if somebody has left the microscope with the draw tube shortened or elongated too much and the next person does not notice it, he may strike the front of one of the objectives on to the slide when rotating the nosepiece. This may cause serious damage. This does not happen when the tube is set at its standard working length. For college and high school laboratories therefore we absolutely recommend the tube of the "fixed length" type. The same holds true for any laboratory where several people use the same microscope. By careful and proper use of the draw tube we can increase or decrease the magnification slightly, depending respectively on whether we elongate it or shorten it. Since the size of the field of view is closely related to magnification, if we elongate the tube we reduce the size of the field, if we shorten the tube we increase it. In drawing or photomicrography these possibilities are sometimes very useful.

The tube of the microscope is movable up and down by means of a "coarse adjustment" which consists of a diagonally cut rack and a pinion, and a "fine adjustment" capable of giving us an extremely slow and fine movement up or down which is essential for the accurate focusing of high power objectives especially the oil immersion lenses. If possible it is better to have a fine adjustment designed in such a way that it does not exert any direct force downward for if, in focusing down with it, one touches the slide, the possibility of damage to the objective or the slide is greatly reduced. Most modern microscopes of good makes are equipped with this safety feature. One must also remember that the possible excursion of the fine adjustment is very short, two to four millimeters, therefore in order not to find that one has reached the limit of its excursion at an awkward moment it is wise to make sure that one starts with it at *the middle* of its possible movement. The different manufacturers each have their own provision to establish this fact. Most fine adjustments are graduated so that one may know how far the tube moves with each complete revolution or fraction thereof, of the fine adjustment buttons. The value of the fine graduations is usually engraved on some part of one of the buttons. This value is usually somewhere between 1 and 3 microns (1 micron = .001 mm). It is obvious therefore that, with some experience, one can make some fairly accurate vertical measurements with a graduated and accurate fine adjustment especially when using very high power objectives, which because of their extremely short depth of focus (the distance above and below the point at which they are in perfect focus which can be seen with a fair degree of clarity), have an almost negligible possible error for measurements in this manner. For this reason many people prefer those fine adjustments of the micrometer screw construction.

Finally, we have "the inclination joint" which enables us to incline the microscope to any comfortable angle and still have it well balanced and stable on the table. This part also permits us to put it in a horizontal position for projecting the image on a vertical screen or down on to the table by means of a prism.

The important mechanical parts of the microscope therefore are: 1, the horse shoe base; 2, the focusing adjustment of the condenser; 3, the stage; 4, the tube (in some cases the binocular body which we shall study later); 5, the coarse adjustment; 6, the fine adjustment; 7, the inclination joint. All these parts are absolutely necessary for best results in a "complete conventional microscope."

In inexpensive stands of compound microscopes the condenser is sometimes eliminated as well as its focusing adjustment, or they may have a condenser, but it cannot be focused. Others have a coarse adjustment only (no fine adjustment), etc. These stands are usually designed for elementary work and to meet the demand where price is a very important factor. Therefore, they have their place, but if possible one's microscope should have at least the possibility of adding to it conveniently later the parts considered essential which we have described above.

Binocular Microscopes

Every person who has two usable eyes finds it easier to read with two eyes than with only one. The same is true when working with a microscope. This is the reason why binocular microscopes were designed and manufactured. Unfortunately, due to the various fine prisms which are necessary in their construction and the tremendous care essential to their proper mounting, these binocular bodies add considerably to the cost of a microscope. However, if possible it is very desirable to use a binocular microscope rather than a monocular, especially if one is going to work with it for long periods of time.

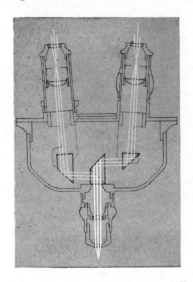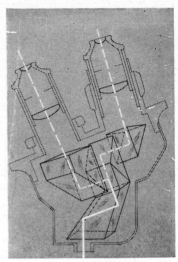

Courtesy Spencer Lens Co.

FIGURE 23

Path of light through vertical and inclined binocular bodies.

Essentially these instruments are exactly the same as the monocular microscopes except that they have a binocular body instead of a single tube. Usually, if one wishes, this body may be removed and a monocular tube put in its place so that a photomicrograph can be taken with the same microscope.

Binocular bodies are made either vertical or inclined. Here again, although the inclined is more expensive because it has one more prism which is particularly difficult to make and more difficult to assemble, it is better to have it because it is so much more comfortable and one does not have to incline the microscope itself in order to attain maximum comfort when sitting at a microscope for two or three hours. It is quite obvious that to incline the microscope itself is only practical

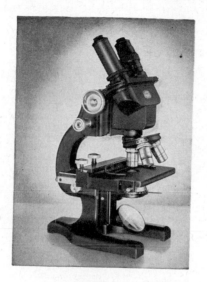

FIGURE 24

Binocular monobjective microscope with inclined prism body.

when using dry permanent specimens. Even with these, unless the stage of the instrument is in a horizontal position, if an oil immersion lens is used the oil slops over the slide on to the stage.

By referring to the illustrations of these binocular assemblies we see that the vertical body has a compound prism directly above the objective. This prism divides the light equally to the right and to the left. On either side of the central prism are the simple prisms which in turn send the light upward to the oculars of the microscope. Naturally binocular microscopes use *paired* oculars. One must be sure of this, for if the oculars used are not paired the results are not satisfactory. The inclined binocular body has an additional prism (placed below the central compound prism) whose sole mission is to change the direction of the light beam. It bends the light somewhere between 30 and 45 degrees depending on the inclination of the binocular body. When this has been done the light is controlled exactly like in the vertical binocular.

Courtesy Bausch & Lomb Opt. Co.

FIGURE 25

Binocular monobjective microscope with vertical prism body.

The tubes which receive the oculars are mounted so that they can be moved laterally away from or toward each other in order to take care of the different possible interpupillary distances. Interpupillary distances vary considerably among people. The average appears to be 60 to 62 millimeters, therefore, the possible adjustment for the tubes is usually designed to accommodate for interpupillary distances from 52 to 70 or 72 mm. Also, since very few people have both their eyes exactly alike, that is, there is usually some difference in the focus of the eyes of the same person, binocular bodies must have some provision to take care of this. Generally one of the ocular tubes is of a variable length so that it can be elongated or shortened within certain practical limits. We shall study the actual use of a binocular microscope in Chapter V.

Another important point often discussed is the manner in which the ocular tubes are mounted. Some manufacturers mount them so that they are parallel to each other. Others recommend the converging tubes. Which are better? There are reasons for both points of view.

Parallel tubes—We are told that there is less eyestrain if the tubes are parallel because when using this construction the eyes of the worker are at rest like when one looks toward the horizon. There is considerable truth in this, but the fact remains that we have seen hundreds of cases of people who simply could not use the parallel tubes; they could not make their eyes relax sufficiently, if you wish, to blend perfectly the two images of the right and left oculars. On the other hand, many people can and do use them in preference to the converging tubes.

Converging tubes—This construction places the tubes

at a slight angle from the perpendicular, 4 degrees for each tube, so that together they form an 8 degree angle. The theory is that this angle equals exactly the convergence of the eyes of most people when they read or work at a table or bench, therefore we are told, the majority of people automatically have this convergence

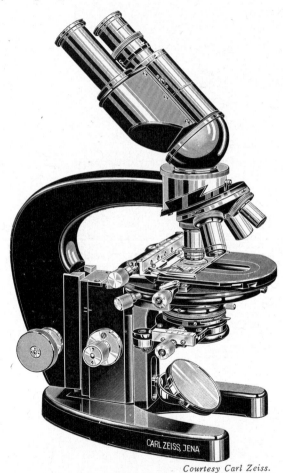

Courtesy Carl Zeiss.

FIGURE 26

A large research binocular microscope.

when they sit to work with a microscope, thus finding it easier and actually of less strain to work with the converging tubes. This is also a good argument and it is a fact that many people who had regretfully given up the idea of using a binocular microscope because they could not blend the two images, have found to their delight that they could use the converging tubes perfectly.

Many people can use either type of construction equally well. Others have a marked preference either way. If there is any doubt in one's mind it is better to try both and then decide which one is better. At this writing one American firm offers either type at no difference in price. Perhaps in time the other manufacturers will do the same.

Before using a binocular body one *must* be sure that the prisms are in perfect alignment for if they are not this causes considerable eyestrain. One feels immediately a definite "pulling" of the eyes and in some cases dizziness. If the displacement of the prisms is only very slight this is not so apparent but the strain is there just the same. It is better to make sure about this by using a stage micrometer slide as an object and see if one gets the slightest double image of the lines. If there is no such double image and the eyes feel comfortable, the binocular body is O.K. We mention this because there is always some danger of displacing the prisms if the instrument has received a hard knock either in shipment or in use. If there is such a displacement the instrument must be sent to the factory for correction.

A very important point to be remembered is that the binocular microscopes need nearly twice as much light as the monocular instruments because only half the light which passes through the objective goes to each eye. It is necessary therefore that when working with a binocular one should use a sufficiently powerful light source. This will be covered more thoroughly later.

Numerical Aperture—(N.A.)

This term "numerical aperture" has been used several times in the preceding pages. We shall now try to explain the meaning of this term as clearly as possible. This is the term suggested by Dr. Abbe to express the ability of a lens to resolve fine details in an object as well as its light gathering capacity in comparison with another lens. It is the value obtained by multiplying the sine of half of its angular aperture by the index of refraction of the medium found between the objective lens and the object. It is expressed mathematically *n sine u*. "n" is the refractive index of the material found between the lens and the object which may be air (refractive index 1.00), water (1.33), cedar oil (1.5), etc. "u" is the greatest angle which the light rays entering the lens make with an imaginary line drawn right down the center of its optical axis, which obviously is half of its total angular aperture. From the above it can be seen immediately that the only way possible to obtain from a lens a numerical aperture greater than 1.00 is to place between the lens and the object some medium which has a refractive index greater than 1.00 like cedar oil. This is why some lenses are designed to work with oil and hence are called oil immersion lenses. We shall study immersion lenses at the end of the chapter.

It is important to remember that one cannot simply increase the numerical aperture of a lens by immersing it in cedar oil, water, etc. The lens itself, must be specially designed to work properly with a medium other than air. By the same token we cannot expect to get good results with an immersion lens unless we *do* use the proper medium between it and the object.

Resolution and Magnification

Since the numerical aperture of objectives governs their resolution it is now time for us to understand this term thoroughly. The resolution of an objective is its ability to resolve or break up an object into its component details so that we can see them. This capacity of a lens is determined by the shortest distance between two lines or points at which they can be seen as two individual lines, instead of just one fat, slightly fuzzy one. The resolving capacity of an objective lens depends on various factors, the wave length of the light which is being used, the index of refraction of the medium in which the object is mounted, the medium between the cover glass and the lens and the greatest angle at which the light rays can enter the objective. It is perfectly possible to calculate the possible resolution of an objective if one knows its N.A.

As we said before, N.A. = n sine u. The human eye is most sensitive to green light which has a wave length of more or less 0.55 microns. The shortest distance at which an objective will show us two lines or points, in other words, its resolution, will be the result obtained by dividing the wave length of the light by the numerical aperture of the objective when *no condenser* is being used, or by two times the numerical aperture if a condenser is being properly used so that the back lens of the objective is entirely filled with light. With a 16 mm objective having an N.A. of 0.25

therefore we would have a resolving capacity of 2.2 microns without a condenser and of 1.1 microns with a condenser. If we used white light with a condenser we would find that an oil immersion objective with an N.A. of 1.40 has a mathematical possible resolution of 0.2 microns.* It is possible to increase resolution by using light of very short wave length like ultraviolet light, but in that case one must photograph the results for the human eye cannot see these rays. With certain specimens it is also possible, by illuminating them with a dark field condenser, to see objects so small that an objective cannot show them properly because its resolution is not sufficient. More of that later.

The power of resolution of an objective will indicate to us what objective it is necessary to use to observe an object if we know its size, but this does not mean that we are going to be able to see it unless we can first magnify it so that it will be within the power of resolution of the *human eye* which has some very definite limitations in this respect. (Also see Proper Magnification for Measurements, Chapter IX.)

The power of resolution of the eyes of various people varies. Some can do better than others. Even the same person can do better on certain days than he can at other times, depending on fatigue, etc. All we can do here is to attempt to give some practical help which will be useful. Generally most people can use a magnification between 500 and 1,000 times the numerical aperture of the objective. For example if we use again an objective with an N.A. of 0.25 we find that it is practical for a person with really good eyes to obtain with it a magnification of 250 diameters. This magnification can

* About the limit of resolution of the human eye.

be reached by using with it a 25x ocular for the objective has a magnification of 10x. Naturally, we could use an ocular of say 30x and thus get a magnification of 300 diameters, but these additional 50 diameters would be "empty magnification," that is, we would not see any more details of the object than we saw with the 250x. One should remember this important point because many students believe that all they have to do to see more details of an object is to use higher and higher oculars. This is not true for when they reach the empty magnification point, any additional magnifying power will be useless in most cases.*

We have said that people with *good* eyes can use to advantage a magnification of 1,000 times the N.A. of the objective, but many people do not have very good eyes. Therefore a good average rule is *to use a magnification no higher than 750 times the N.A. of the objective.*

The Immersion Objectives

As their name indicates these objectives should *always* be used with their front lens immersed in a drop of the medium *for which they were designed.* This medium has a certain definite refractive index and it may be cedar oil, glycerine, water, etc. This is necessary because due to their N.A. they require the use of a cone of light of wide angle. If such a cone is not used it is impossible to obtain the best results of which they are capable. Such a cone of light cannot be obtained if we do not put between the front lens of the objective and the object (or cover glass) *and also* be-

---

* The exceptions would be for some measurements and for some photomicrographs.

tween the condenser and the bottom of the slide the
necessary medium. This medium is usually cedar oil
because its refractive index is so near that of optical
glass. Hence the term "oil immersion objectives." The
cedar oil in practice acts like an elastic optical glass
through which the light rays travel from the condenser
in a straight line. Only in this way is it possible to
take advantage of the complete rated N.A. of an oil
immersion objective. If an objective is not an immersion
objective its highest possible N.A. would be 1.00, in
other words, it is somewhat limited in its possible resolution, but if it is an immersion objective it can be calculated for as high as 1.40 or more and thus we can
reach high magnifications with excellent resolution.
Here is a good example. Let us take two objectives
(manufactured by most good houses) which are of the
same equivalent focus and the same magnification but
of different N.A. Let us see what is the highest magnification each can give us without "empty magnification" and thus we shall see the necessity of immersion
lenses. We shall compare two 3 mm objectives both
having a power of 60x. One is dry and has an N.A.
of 0.95 (near the maximum for a dry objective), the
other is an oil immersion objective with an N.A. of
1.40. We apply our "thousand times" rule and find
that the dry lens can give us a magnification (free of
"empty magnification") of 950 diameters whereas the
oil immersion lens can give us 1,400; 450 diameters
more! It is because of this, regardless of the fact that
the immersion lenses are necessarily more difficult to
use, that all persons who must work with high magnifications, like the bacteriologists, use them in preference to the dry lenses.

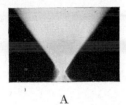

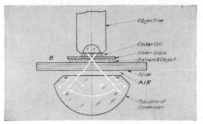

FIGURE 27

Comparative Cones of Light. (A) N.A. 1.30 without immersion of condenser. (B) N.A. 1.30 with immersion of condenser.

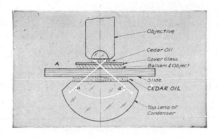

FIGURE 28

Reduced illuminating cone when condenser is not in immersion contact with slide.

It is perfectly practical and possible to use an oil immersion lens without putting any oil between the condenser and the slide, but if we use it in this manner we must remember that we cannot obtain with it its full capacity of resolution because its N.A. has been reduced to about 1.00 * even although it may be marked with a higher N.A. value. This is due to the fact that since there is no direct medium, free of air, of a high refractive index between the condenser and the front lens of the objective, the cone of light which enters the objective cannot have a sufficiently wide angle which will give us much more than N.A. 1.00. It also follows

* Since the refractive index of air is taken as 1.00.

therefore that if the condenser used has a maximum N.A. rating of a less value than that of the objective, the maximum N.A. which we can get from the objective is that of the condenser even although the objective is rated with a higher numerical aperture. If we have a microscope equipped with a condenser N.A. 1.25 it would be somewhat foolish to buy an objective of N.A. 1.40 for it could not give us much more than 1.25. We should always "balance" our optical system in order to get the highest N.A. of an objective, otherwise, to some extent, the higher cost of a high aperture objective is wasted.

CHAPTER III

ILLUMINATION

It is impossible to obtain the maximum efficiency of a microscope unless one fully understands the very important subject of microscope illumination. The object under observation must be illuminated so as to give complete advantage of the full possibilities of our optical system.

In the previous chapter we investigated the importance and use of the microscope condensers, but we cannot stop there; we must go further and investigate the sources of the light which enters the condenser as well as the correct use of these light sources. Actually one should consider the microscope to begin at the source of light which is to be used to illuminate the specimen.

Important as is this subject, it is surprising how little attention is paid to it by the majority of people who work with a microscope. We do not refer to the careful and experienced microscopists who, naturally, do use proper illumination correctly, but rather to the vast number of earnest scientists, technicians and students who simply have never bothered to be careful about this point and who because of this are not very likely to see all that their microscope can show them. This chapter should be of some practical help to them.

The following is an actual case which illustrates the question quite well. A graduate student working for his Ph.D. saved, after considerable effort, enough money to purchase a beautiful research binocular microscope with apochromatic objectives, etc. When he got it he was very disappointed because he did not see the details in his slides any better; as a matter of fact, he did not see them as well, as when he used the old monocular, inexpensive microscope with which he had worked previously. It was found upon investigation that the young fellow was using the same small 15 watt substage lamp with his new microscope which he had found satisfactory with his old monocular. Result: insufficient light for his new binocular. Also he was not focusing his condenser carefully because he never had found it necessary with his monocular, but his new research microscope was properly equipped with a highly corrected achromatic and aplanatic condenser which required very much more careful focusing than the simple Abbe condenser he had used previously. When these two points were corrected and he learned something about proper illumination, our budding Ph.D. soon found that he could see more details better and with more comfort.

The light used with a microscope may be daylight such as that found near a window, or artificial light from a microscope lamp of some kind. The daylight which is usually considered best is that which comes to us reflected from a white cloud in the northern sky. Since, however, white clouds are not always available when we want them and since a great deal of microscope work is done during dark days or after dark, the great majority of microscopists are using exclusively artificial light.

This is partly the reason why all microscope manufacturers lay so much emphasis on "microscope lamps."

Courtesy Spencer Lens Co.
FIGURE 29

Substage lamp—May be placed under or in front of the microscope.

The most important reason however is that manufacturers recognize very definitely the importance of proper illumination in the performance of their microscopes. Some have gone so far as to actually incorporate the proper lighting unit in their research microscopes so that this point cannot possibly be neglected by the microscopist. Unfortunately, those complete equipments are necessarily very expensive, but if one is careful it is possible to get good results with a less costly lighting unit.

There are many types of microscope lamps available, the little ones called substage lamps which may be used under the microscope in place of the mirror, others more complete, equipped with a more powerful illuminant, and finally the very complete lamps with condensing lenses, reflector, iris aperture diaphragm, filters, etc.

Now let us look into this lighting problem and make some practical suggestions which will fit the great majority of cases. We shall consider first the illumination of transparent objects.

After many years of experience most well-known microscopists seem to agree that the three usual methods of illumination are:

> A—An approximation to critical illumination
> B—Critical Illumination
> C—Köhler Illumination

The two best are B and C, *but the first is adequate for most purposes* where very high powers are not being used and where the finest possible results are not absolutely essential. The disadvantage of B and C is that they require some "fussing" to obtain them properly, but the results justify this additional trouble at high magnifications.

Now let us see how each type is obtained and used.

A—*An approximation to Critical Illumination* can be obtained with any microscope equipped with a condenser. We can use daylight or artificial light. The all important point is *to fill with light the back lens of the objective which is being used* without at the same time having additional light rays which will tend to cloud the image. This is controlled by means of the iris diaphragm of the condenser and by focusing the condenser.

Let us take a lamp like the one illustrated in fig. 29 which we shall place under the condenser of our microscope after removing the microscope mirror. We center it as carefully as possible. These little lamps usually have a 10 or 15 watt bulb with a reflector in back and a blue ground glass at the opening. Sometimes this glass is a daylight glass which is not entirely transparent if it is ground. The white light obtained with the Corning daylight glass approximates more closely real daylight and hence is often preferred. Obviously what we are doing when we use this type of lamp is placing our white cloud under the microscope right where we want it and where it won't get away from us. How come? The bulb of the lamp aided by the reflector illuminates the glass filter brilliantly so that the filter itself becomes our light source, not the bulb but the filter is our light.

To get real critical illumination as we shall see later, we would have to focus with our condenser our light source on the object at the same time that the object is in focus. We cannot do this however, when we use a ground glass or a glass which is not entirely transparent. Its grain would show on the object and we would harm our image, but we can do everything else required for critical illumination and thus obtain very good results.

Our substage lamp is under the condenser, we have made sure *that the condenser is almost touching the bottom of the slide or slightly lower if the slide is very thin;* also that the object is focused in the regular manner (example and routine in Chapter V). Now we see our object well illuminated, but we want to be sure we have an approximation to critical illumination. We remove the ocular of the microscope and look down the tube to see the back lens of the objective, we close the iris diaphragm of the condenser which we can now see on the back lens of the objective. Now we open it slowly until its margin just about coincides with that of the back lens of the objective, in other words the iris opening should appear the *same size* as the back lens of the objective we are using. If we have a modern microscope having its condenser graduated to the various N.A. values it delivers at different apertures of the

Courtesy Spencer Lens Co.

FIGURE 30

Chalet type lamp.

iris we can now see that the opening we are using just about equals the numerical aperture of our objective. Now our illumination is right for good results and we won't have any harmful rays spoiling our image. Naturally if our condenser is graduated we can simply set the iris to an opening which equals the N.A. of the objective in use and we won't have to be looking down the tube at the back lens of the objective. This provided that the condenser is not too low nor too high.

If we are using a more powerful lamp such as fig. 30 we place it in front of the microscope and direct its light upward by means of the *plain mirror*, not the concave. The same is true if we use this type of illumination with one of the more complete lamps like figs. 34 or 35. Basically, the only difference is that the stronger lamps illuminate the glass filter more brightly and hence our light source gives us more light.

Let us repeat here that a binocular microscope *must* have enough light before we can get the full benefit of the binocular body. A good rule for a binocular for all powers is to use a bulb of at least 50 or 60 watts in the "Chalet" type of lamp. Better yet, one of the better lamps like figs. 34 or 35 which have condensers, an iris diaphragm and a clear blue and a ground glass or a Corning daylight glass illuminated by a 100 watt bulb. In using this type of lamp equipped with an iris place it about 6 to 10 inches away from the mirror and open the iris of the lamp all the way for all objectives from 16 mm up (16, 25, 32, 40, etc.). For the 8 mm objectives (20x) close the lamp iris to an opening of about 1.5″ for the 4 mm to about one inch and for the oil immersion to about ¼ to ½ inch opening. If we have too much light to suit us don't let us close the iris diaphragm of the condenser and thus unbalance the optical system. Let us place instead neutral tint filters between the lamp and the mirror of the microscope.

All the above is true for the correct "A" type of illumination. There are however certain exceptions. For example:

1. We may not care about the finest resolution of a specimen but simply about its outline. In that case we can increase contrast by closing the iris of the condenser below the N.A. of the objective, or we may lower the condenser to the desired point. However we must remember that if we do this we are reducing the capacity of our optical system to show us fine details. Undoubtedly, however, sometimes one must sacrifice resolution for the sake of contrast. Here's a good example of what happens when the optical system is unbalanced in this way or rather of how much more

detail of an object can be seen when the optical system is properly balanced:

Take a good specimen of pleurisigma angulatum (a diatome) and using a good 4 mm objective with a 10x ocular focus carefully one of the diatomes in the center of the field with the iris of the condenser closed down to about 0.30. We can now see its shape and general outlines beautifully, but we cannot see the black dots. Now open the iris of the condenser slowly and when an aperture of about 0.5 or 0.6 is reached suddenly we can see the dots quite well, the existence of which we could not even suspect otherwise. Now lower the condenser slowly without touching the diaphragm, again contrast increases but the dots disappear. This incidentally is a good critical test for a 4 mm objective N.A.0.66, but don't try to resolve the dots without a condenser.

2. We may have a very transparent object which cannot be seen unless we close the iris or lower the condenser to gain more contrast. However, if we want to see its fine details we must stain and illuminate it properly.

If we are using a very low power objective in order to get a very large field (a 32, 40, 48 mm) it is usually necessary to remove the top lens of the condenser in order to fill the back lens of the objective with light. If the condenser is not divisible we must try the concave surface of the mirror or remove the condenser altogether and use our concave mirror instead. Since with these very low power objectives resolution is not very important we can take certain liberties which would be really harmful with high magnifications.

All the above covers our "A" illumination. This is

the type which is most generally used for good routine work because it is the easiest and gives satisfactory results if one remembers the *two* important points about it which we shall now repeat, a, to fill with light the back lens of the objective while balancing the N.A. of the condenser with that of the objective in use; b, to have the condenser almost touching the slide or slightly lower if the slide is very thin.

B—*Critical Illumination* is the same as "A" but *we must focus our light source on the object* when it is also in focus. This will give us much better results but we need a lamp which will give us fairly parallel rays and we cannot have anything but transparent clear filters (no ground or semi-opaque glass) between the condensers of the lamp and the microscope mirror.

Many of the important discoveries attained with the microscope by early microscopists were made with critical illumination. They used the flame of an oil lamp as their light source and focused it very carefully upon their object with their condenser. Unfortunately however, the flame wavered at times if there were any

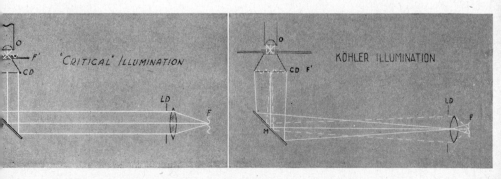

FIGURE 31

Critical illumination.

FIGURE 32

Kohler illumination.

air currents in the room and with the advent of electric light bulbs it was found that their filaments could not properly illuminate the entire field of many objectives. The ribbon filament bulbs took care of this fairly well but they are quite expensive and a transformer is necessary for use on A.C. current. If only D.C. current is available special wiring must be installed. Fig. 37 shows

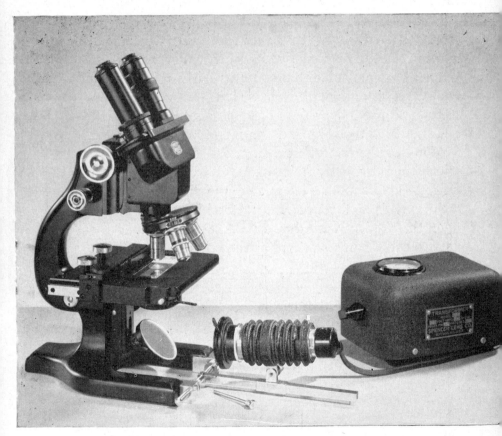

Courtesy Spencer Le

FIGURE 33

Universal low voltage lamp with variable transformer.

us a lamp specially designed for critical illumination. It gives us parallel rays and has all the necessary adjustments. A ribbon filament bulb is used.

If the best possible results are required with a standard laboratory lamp like fig. 34, the Köhler illumination is recommended.

C–Köhler Illumination. When we really want to see a better image, especially with objectives of 44x or more up to the oil immersion lenses, the results obtained with the Köhler system will surprise and delight us. If

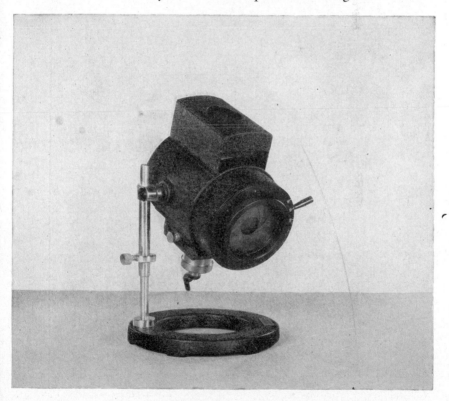

Courtesy Spencer Lens Co.

FIGURE 34

Adjustable laboratory lamp with iris diaphragm.

we have a specimen perfectly illuminated with the A method described above and we then illuminate it with the Köhler method it seems that we have removed a thin veil which was preventing us from seeing very clearly the fine details of the object. The same is true when perfect critical illumination is used. Most of the photomicrographs used in text books are taken with Köhler illumination. This is the reason why many students cannot see objects as clearly as they appear in

Courtesy Bausch & Lomb Opt. Co.

FIGURE 35

Spherical lamp equipped with aspheric condenser and iris diaphragm.

the photomicrographs of text books. If they use the proper illumination however, they will see details as well or better with their own microscope.

Courtesy Spencer Lens Co.
FIGURE 36

Research Microscope lamp with holder for water cell and filters and focusable condensers.

Let us prepare our standard laboratory lamp for Köhler illumination, again one as in fig. 34. We place it 8 or 10 inches away from the mirror of the microscope, and direct the light beam to the center of the mirror after removing all filters. We now move the bulb back about ½ inch from its farthest possible forward position. At this point if we have closed the iris diaphragm of the condenser we can see it by means of the mirror of our microscope if we look at the mirror from near the same position where the lamp is located. We focus the filaments of the bulb on the iris diaphragm of the condenser (it is better to get one of the center filaments over the middle of the iris) by moving the bulb of the lamp slightly forward or backward. Now we open the iris diaphragm of the condenser to about the same N.A. of the objective. We close the iris of the lamp as far as it will go and we put in the lamp the

clear blue glass filter. If the condenser of the microscope is at the right height we can now see the iris of
the lamp superimposed on the object under observation
provided we have properly focused it before with "A"
illumination. If the iris is not in focus move the condenser up or down slightly with its focusing adjustment. When it is in focus we open the iris of the lamp
so it coincides with the field we are viewing. If we
have too much light we reduce it with neutral tint filters
to the required intensity. Now we have Köhler illumination. If we take off the ocular of the microscope

Courtesy Bausch & Lomb Opt. Co.

FIGURE 37

Research microscope lamp for critical illumination with
ribbon filament bulb.

we can see the back lens of the objective filled with light and the filaments of the lamp appear to be right on this back lens. Unfortunately many lamp iris dia-

Courtesy Carl Zeiss.

FIGURE 38

Small low voltage lamp with Rubin glass cylinder, aspheric condenser and iris diaphragm.

phragms do not close down far enough so that we can see the image of the iris when an oil immersion lens is being used, but if we check this point with the 4 mm objective the illumination is also very close to perfection when we swing to the immersion lens provided we open the iris of the condenser to the proper N.A. value.

If our lamp is equipped with a ribbon filament bulb we proceed in the same manner being careful to focus the ribbon on the center of the iris diaphragm of the condenser. If our lamp has a focusing adjustment for its condensing system we do not have to move the bulb back and forth, we simply set it near its maximum forward position and use the focusing mechanism of the condensing system for the final adjustment.

We have seen therefore that the recommended methods for illuminating transparent objects when using a microscope equipped with a condenser are:

A—A close approximation to Critical Illumination
B—Critical Illumination
C—Köhler Illumination

Conclusions: From a practical standpoint to fit the great majority of cases we suggest:

1. Use "A" illumination for all lower power objectives up to and including the 8 mm 20x lenses. Also for general laboratory routine work with the higher powers, including oil immersion.

2. For the very best results with high power objectives such as 4 mm, 3 mm, and oil immersion objectives use either Critical Illumination "B," if we have a good specially designed lamp for this type of lighting, or Köhler illumination "C."

Courtesy E. Leitz, Inc.

FIGURE 39

Arc lamp with automatic feed of carbons.

3. For photomicrography use whenever possible, Köhler Illumination.

4. If possible it is best to have a lamp which can be used properly for at least A and C.

Recently various manufacturers have put on the market small very efficient microscope lamps equipped with low voltage bulbs. These are good when properly designed but one must use them with a transformer on A.C. current. Otherwise special wiring, a convertor or special resistances are necessary for D.C. current.

Accessories for Fluorescent Illumination

Another recently developed method of illumination for transparent objects is that of illuminating them with

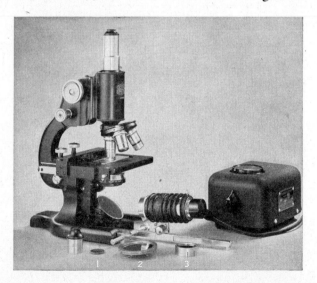

Courtesy Spencer Lens Co.

FIGURE 40

Accessories for fluorescence illumination of acid fast bacteria—for use with low voltage lamp. 1—yellow disc for eyepiece; 2—aluminized mirror; 3—ultraviolet transmitting filter for lamp.

ultra violet light after treating them with some fluorescent solution. Fluorescent materials emit visible light when irradiated with invisible ultra violet radiation. Some do this naturally while others must be "stained" with a fluorescent solution. The detailed examination requires an intense source of ultra violet radiation and special equipment but simple attachments are available to be used with small microscope lamps of the type mentioned in the previous paragraph and any standard monocular microscope. These equipments (fig. 40) have proved very practical and useful for many materials including the identification of acid fast bacteria.

Dark Field Illumination

Although this is also a method of illuminating transparent materials, it is quite different from those described in the previous pages and must be treated separately. The effect of this type of illumination may be compared with light rays projected with a steropticon in a dark room when minute dust particles can be seen floating in the air which could not be seen when the room was well lighted. Minute objects capable of reflecting light can be seen better over a dark field than over a light field. Therefore the use of the dark field may reveal to us objects which are either too transparent or too small to be seen over a light field. If these particles are so small that the resolving power of the objective is not sufficient to give us a good idea of their form, etc. at least it may show us that they actually exist even although we cannot study their shape or measure them. It is possible however, to get a good idea of their number in a definite field and to make a close guess as to their size. The stronger the light we

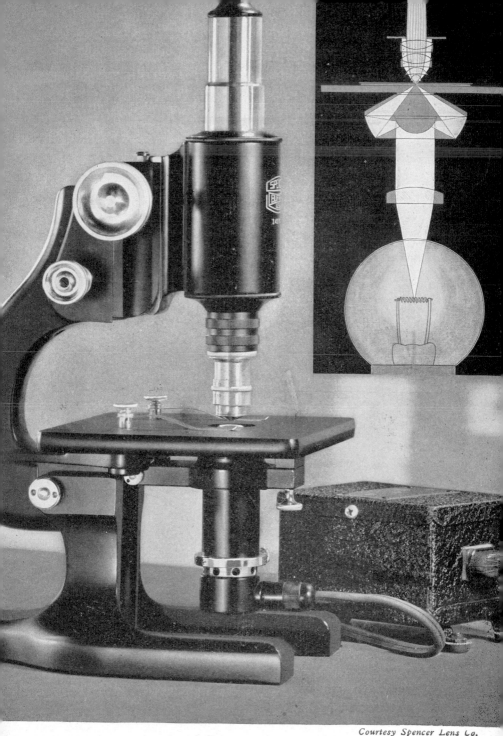

FIGURE 41

A special dark field microscope with light source
built in under the condenser.

use the smaller the particles that can be seen on the dark field.

There are various methods which can be used to obtain this result. The one most generally used is that of the dark field condenser, fig. 42. This type of condenser is so constructed that it will not permit any direct light rays to enter the objective of the microscope. The hollow cone of light produced by these condensers is focused on the object or specimen and when we view it we see it as a self-luminous object in an almost entirely black field. There are various kinds of dark field condensers, that is, the formulae used in their construction vary but all the good ones give us more or less similar results. Some dark field condensers

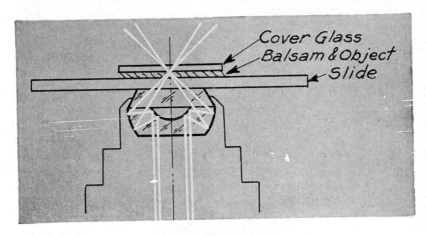

Cover Glass
Balsam & Object
Slide

Courtesy Spencer Lens Co.

FIGURE 42
Path of light through a dark field condenser.

have their powerful light source incorporated in their construction, others require the use of a separate light source such as a microscope lamp or *direct* sunlight.

To use these condensers it is first necessary to remove from the microscope the regular light field condenser and to put in its place the dark field unit. Let us consider first the use of a dark field condenser with an independent microscope lamp.

First of all we must emphasize the fact that the *illuminant must be very powerful*. A substage lamp or a chalet, or table lamp simply *will not do*, yet it is surprising how many people try to use dark field condensers with inadequate light units. For a monocular microscope we must have *at least* a 100 watt bulb if we use a lamp like fig. 34 or 35. For a binocular a 200 watt bulb in the same kind of lamp, an arc lamp or some other type which will deliver sufficient light. Let us repeat again that it is a waste of time to expect good results with a dark field condenser if we do not use a sufficiently powerful light.

It is necessary to use a microscope slide of the correct thickness for the condenser being used. This is usually somewhere between 1.10 and 1.45 mm. Manufacturers generally mark their dark field condensers with the thickness of slides which must be used with them for best results. If the wrong slide thickness is used the cone of light cannot be properly focused upon the object and the results are not satisfactory.

Since it is essential that the condenser be perfectly centered in relation to the objective, a good dark field condenser has some provision to center it very exactly, usually centering screws which work against a spring are provided.

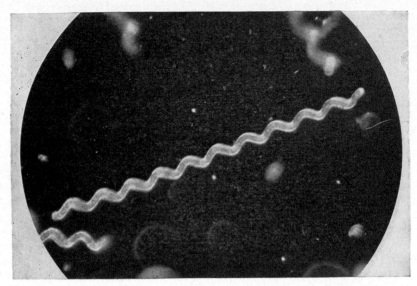

Courtesy Spencer Lens Co.

FIGURE 43

Spirulina Jennerii at 360X (dark field illumination).

The slide, the cover glass, and the top lens of the condenser must be perfectly clean and free of any scratches, and there must *always* be oil between the condenser and the bottom of the slide. If an objective is used which has an N.A. higher than 1.00 this N.A. must be reduced to less than 1.00 by a "funnel stop" which is inserted into the back mount of the objective, or by means of an iris diaphragm if the objective is so equipped.* Usually the N.A. is thus reduced to about 0.85. This means therefore that before we use an oil immersion lens for dark field we must reduce its numerical aperture. The only exception to this would be a dark field combination designed for a higher N.A. Most dark field condensers however are designed for use with an N.A. of 1.00 or lower than 1.00.

* Unless the dark field condenser is designed for a higher N.A.

The proper technique for use with an oil immersion lens would be as follows: *

We put our dark field condenser in its proper position being sure that we can move it up high enough to just touch the bottom of a slide placed on the stage or mechanical stage of the microscope. Our microscope lamp is placed in front of the microscope 8 to 10 inches away from the mirror. If any filter is used on the lamp such as a blue glass it must be entirely transparent, no ground glass or a semi-opaque filter of any kind should be in place. A water filter to cool the light placed between the lamp and the mirror is often very useful. The beam of light is directed toward the center of the mirror of the microscope and reflected upward toward the condenser.

The 16 mm 10x objective of the microscope is used for centering the condenser. We focus down with it carefully and we can then see the "centering ring" which is cut on the top lens of most dark field condensers. When this ring is in focus it appears as a bright luminous ring on a dark field. If it is not right in the middle of the field we center the condenser by means of the centering screws or the mechanism supplied by the manufacturer. We now move the mirror slightly to make sure this ring appears at its brightest and we then leave it in that position.

We now make sure that the N.A. of our oil immersion lens has been reduced either with the funnel stop or with the iris diaphragm if it has one. We have a clean slide ready as well as a cover glass and we put on it our specimen and cover it immediately with our cover glass. We put a good drop of oil on top of our

* Dark field condensers are also used to advantage with dry objectives.

condenser and lower it a little, the slide is put on the stage and the condenser raised slowly until there's a good oil contact between the bottom of the slide and the top lens of the condenser. This contact must be free of air bubbles which if present will spoil our image. The oil immersion objective is now swung to its working position. A drop of oil is placed on top of the cover glass and the oil immersion lens lowered into it until it's almost touching the cover glass (this cover glass must be very thin, a zero or a No. 1 if possible) and that there's a good oil contact between the objective and the cover glass. We now look through the eyepiece of the microscope and focus very carefully *with the fine adjustment* until the object is in perfect focus.

If we have done all this correctly we now have our objects brilliantly illuminated in an otherwise dark field. If we have air bubbles in the oil either below or above the slide they will spoil the results and the only remedy is to start all over again. These bubbles can be seen if the ocular is removed from the microscope and one looks down the tube. If the light does not seem quite what it should be move the condenser up or down a little. A point will be found, if the right slide thickness is being used, where the results are perfect. After one is finished using the dark field it is a good idea to remove the funnel stop from the oil immersion lens immediately, otherwise it might be forgotten and when using the objective for regular work the results will not be very good.

As can be seen by the above the proper use of the dark field condenser is not very easy, it requires practice and care. Perhaps this plus its cost has prevented its more common use even although more and more people are beginning to realize its possibilities. This is the reason why special dark field microscopes have been developed which are a great aid to the laboratories where many dark field examinations must be made daily. These equipments greatly simplify the use of the dark field for they have their light source built in as part of the substage and no centering of the condenser is necessary. Also the objective always has an iris diaphragm.

The use of the electric dark field condensers is also easier. This is the type most popular with the U. S. Army for instance because it reduces the chances of poor results to a minimum and can be used on standard routine microscopes. These condensers have a built-in light of low voltage which can be used with the proper resistance on A.C. or D.C. current of 110 or 220 volts or with a 6 volt storage battery. Their use is very similar to that described above but the light problem is eliminated. They must be centered however in the same manner and instructions of the manufacturer must be rigidly followed to get the best results.

When direct sunlight is used (a method not uncommon in the tropics) with a dark field condenser, it is necessary to place the microscope where direct sunlight will fall on the mirror of the microscope shading the rest of it in some manner. This light is then used exactly the same as that from a microscope lamp and it is perfectly satisfactory. The trouble is that it is not always possible or convenient to get direct sunlight.

Oblique Illumination

This type of illumination is used very little nowadays. It is sometimes used to obtain a little better resolving power of certain specimens with a given objective than is possible with the usual lighting methods. Its disadvantage is that color fringes are usually visible in the field, hence its use is now generally confined to the study of objects such as diatomes.

Courtesy Spencer Lens Co.
FIGURE 44
Oblique illumination.

It is accomplished by sending light upward to the condenser with a decentered mirror or by decentering the condenser slightly. Another method is to permit the light to enter the condenser only from one side. Most research microscopes are provided with some means to illuminate the object with oblique light. At times, and for special purposes this type of illumination is useful.

Illumination of Opaque Objects

Since transmitted light is not possible when an opaque object must be examined, the illumination of this type of object must necessarily be quite different. Opaque objects must be illuminated from above in some manner. The usual methods are as follows:

If low power objectives are used, since these objectives have a long working distance (plenty of space between their lowest lens and the object when they are focused), it is possible to direct a beam of light directly upon the object from in front or the side of the microscope. Some objects show us more details if this light beam strikes them quite obliquely, others as near from the top as possible. It is necessary to experiment with a given object and thus determine which angle is best. Once this is done the microscope lamp can be placed conveniently to give us the best results. A good example that comes to mind is the problem faced by a certain Board of Health laboratory in a large city where certain bacteria cultures in petri dishes had to be examined under fairly low magnifications (about 30 to 40x). The cultures were so opaque that transmitted light was useless. Various angles of incident light were tried and finally the best results for that particular problem were obtained when the beam of light was directed at an angle of about 85 degrees from the perpendicular. At this point the contrast was perfect and the details of the bacteria colonies could be seen very well. No other angle of illumination could be used to advantage. Since it is difficult if not impossible to set down a definite rule for this type of illumination, the trial and error method is the only one open to us. In certain cases two or more lamps with light rays coming from different angles and directions are necessary for best results.

If high power objectives are used, since these objectives have short working distances and thus we cannot get the proper amount of light on to the object in the above mentioned manner, we must send the light down through the objective itself. This means that the objective must act as a condenser as well as perform its regular duties. This is accomplished by the use of the vertical illuminator which is placed between the objective and the tube of the microscope. These illuminators basically consist of a mount which receives the objective at the lower end and is attached to the tube of the microscope at the other end. In the center it has a reflector which will send the light down through the objective. The light reaches the reflector through an

Courtesy Spencer Lens Co.

FIGURE 45
Vertical illuminators.

opening in the side of the mount. In this way the object is properly and brilliantly illuminated and from then on the optical system of the microscope performs its usual function. The proper use of the vertical illuminator will be better explained in Chapter VII where the metallurgical microscope is discussed. Here however, we shall describe the various possibilities and give some useful information.

Some of these vertical illuminators are equipped with a reflector made of a transparent piece of very thin glass. These are called plate glass vertical illuminators. Others have a small prism which is a little to the side of the top lens of the objective, in other words the light goes down at a slight angle from the optical axis of the objective and its N.A. is thus somewhat reduced. Others use a small mirror cut in the shape of a half moon mounted in the same manner as the prism. Finally others have a combination of both the plate glass and the prism, that is, either can be placed into its working position at a moment's notice. As can be seen immediately, since the amount of light loss is very much greater with the plate glass type, much more light can be placed on the object with the prism or mirror type with a given light source. On the other hand, with the plate glass type we do not make half the top lens of the objective useless (because the prism and the mirror are opaque) and therefore we do not materially reduce the N.A. of the objective. A good practical rule which in practice works out satisfactorily in most cases is to:

A—For the lower power objectives such as 25 mm, 16 mm and 8 mm where N.A. is not all important use the prism or mirror type for it is then possible to get the maximum possible light. This can always be reduced if necessary by diminishing the strength of the light source.

B—For the higher power objectives such as the 4 mm, 3 mm and oil immersion objectives where their high N.A. is very important, use the plate glass type of illuminator.

C—If we can acquire only one vertical illuminator and we cannot have the combination of both types and the use of all powers of objectives is necessary, in other words, if we must choose between the plate glass and the prism type for all work, then it is better to decide on the plate glass.

Some vertical illuminators have their light source

built on the side and thus an independent light source is not necessary. Also they have iris diaphragms which are helpful and a receptacle for colored filters. *The use of a green filter* is of considerable aid when studying metallurgical specimens. These complete electric vertical illuminators are fine but much more expensive than the simpler types.*

Recently certain new developments in the way of

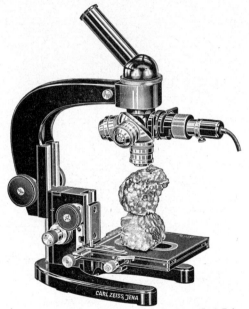

Courtesy Carl Zeiss.

FIGURE 46

Epi W condenser for vertical dark field illumination, light coming from all sides of object—convertible for bright field illumination.

vertical illuminators have appeared in the market, the Leitz "Ultropack" and the Zeiss "Epi W Condenser." Reichert also has developed similar equipment. These illuminators employ a conical ring of light which travels

* See also Chapter VII Metallurgical Microscopes.

down the outside of the objective to be focused beneath it on the object. These outfits consist of special objectives and reflectors combined with a specially designed light source and condensing system. They are

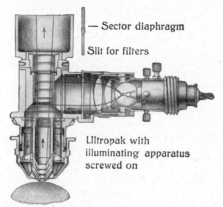

— Sector diaphragm

Slit for filters

Ultropak with illuminating apparatus screwed on

Courtesy E. Leitz, Inc.

FIGURE 47

Ultropak illuminator showing path of light rays.

very good but until now very expensive. It is quite possible that American manufacturers will develop in time such equipment also as it has real possibilities and is not difficult to use. These illuminators offer a method of studying living cells in situ and should yield very interesting results.

Chapter IV

THE MICROTOME

Before taking up in a general way the question of the preparation of materials (Chapter V) so that we may examine them with a high power microscope, it is proper to describe an instrument which is very closely related to the microscope, and also to explain its use in a way which we hope will be helpful. This instrument is the microtome.

Without its development the study of tissues (both plant and animal) would have been practically impossible. Such tissues must be cut extremely thin before they can be properly studied with a microscope. The development of the microtome to its present perfection therefore has paralleled very closely that of the microscope. The urgent necessity for these instruments was felt as early as the middle of the 18th century, and very logically, both the microtome and the optical microscope have just about reached the limit of their perfection at the same time.

The proper technique in the use of the microtome is as important and as complex as that of the microscope.

We have heard the microtome described as "a glorified slicing machine." Actually this is not an inaccurate description. The microtome is simply a cutting machine capable of slicing material to an almost unbelievable thinness. Dr. Richards defines it as "an instrument for cutting thin sections of materials too large or not sufficiently transparent for direct examination with the microscope." Any material not so hard or dense that the edge of the microtome knife is destroyed may be sectioned. Some specimens may be cut with the microtome as they are found, others require extensive pretreatment and embedding in a supporting medium.

Basically there are two general types of microtomes. Those on which the specimen to be cut is held in one position and the knife drawn across it and those on which the knife is rigidly held and the object passed across the knife edge. In both cases the object is moved

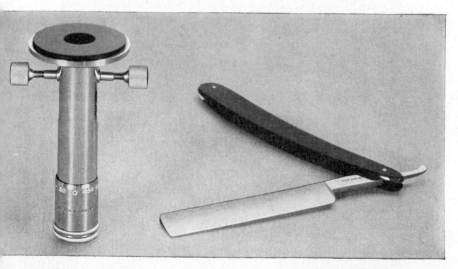

Courtesy Bausch & Lomb Opt. Co.

FIGURE 48

Hand microtome and razor.

a predetermined distance toward the plane of the cutting edge after every stroke. The former or "moving blade" types are referred to as "sliding microtomes," and the latter or "stationary blade" types as "rotary microtomes."

In the sliding microtome class we find the small, inexpensive hand and table microtomes, the clinical freezing microtomes and finally the small and large precision sliding microtomes which vary from each other in their size, feed, etc.

Courtesy Spencer Lens Co.

FIGURE 49
Table microtome.

The rotary microtomes also have many variations. There are the little models for students, the larger and more accurate college laboratory models and finally, the very fine precision research and hospital instruments. Some of these large models may be driven by a motor with a foot control thus cutting down to a minimum the labor of fine sectioning.

There is still a third type which is sometimes favored for cutting sections of large diameter (fig. 52) which looks like a sliding microtome but which actually operates by the Minot principle of moving the object across the knife. This construction has its merits for it allows the use of a very large clamp while the knife is held very rigidly at both ends on the solid slideways.

In the sliding models the knife cuts horizontally, while in the rotary models it cuts in a vertical plane, that is, with the edge of the knife pointing upward. In the type described in the previous paragraph the knife is also used in the horizontal position.

Generally, the large sliding microtomes are used for material embedded in celloidin, for cutting frozen sections with the aid of a freezing attachment and for material which is being cut "as is" without any embedding or only with a supporting medium around it such as pith or cork. Very satisfactory sections can also be cut of material embedded in paraffin. The sliding instrument is not used very generally to cut paraffin sections because it is not as easy to get good ribbons, that is, to get one section to adhere to another by its edge and thus form a ribbon. These ribbons can then be placed on a slide and the sections studied in their proper order after having been stained.

The rotary microtomes are used almost exclusively for cutting paraffin embedded sections. It is possible to get beautiful ribbons with them and they are fast and accurate. It is also possible to cut celloidin sections with a rotary microtome with the aid of a special knife

clamp which holds the knife at an angle instead of horizontal. However it is difficult to keep the surfaces of
the block and knife properly lubricated with alcohol.
Therefore the sliding microtome is preferable for
celloidin.

Courtesy Spencer Lens Co.

FIGURE 50

Clinical Microtome with CO_2 freezing attachment.

The small microtomes of the sliding type can be used
for elementary work of all types where great precision
and very fine sections are not necessary. Their cost
is very much less.

Recommendations:

For high school or hobby work where great accuracy
is not necessary a hand or a table microtome. A fine
microtome knife is not necessary for these instruments.
An old-fashioned razor, good and sharp, or a safety
razor blade (preferably held in a razor blade holder)
will do very nicely.

For college botanical laboratories a small sliding microtome with or without the automatic feeding mechanism.

For histological, pathological, and general biology laboratories in colleges and universities the rotary microtomes.

For hospitals, the ideal is a good rotary, a good sliding and a freezing microtome. If only one microtome can be had and the work will be about evenly divided between paraffin and celloidin embedded material, then the sliding microtome with a freezing attachment

Courtesy Spencer Lens Co.

FIGURE 51

Sliding microtome.

is advisable. If most of the work is with paraffin, a rotary microtome is a necessity. A freezing attachment cannot be used with a rotary microtome and therefore if any freezing work is to be done a freezing microtome is necessary. If some celloidin work has to be done, the special knife clamp mentioned previously can be secured for the rotary microtome.

General Information for Sectioning of Materials

For proper sectioning most materials must be embedded in something, a matrix, which will support them properly, otherwise they will be crushed or damaged and a good section is impossible. Let us consider first those materials where embedding is not absolutely necessary or is impractical, then we shall take up celloidin and paraffin embedding and the freezing technique.

Material "as is"—If the material is moderately dense and sections need not be thinner than 15 to 20 microns it can be sectioned without any embedding. The less woody plant tissues are better adapted to this method than animal tissues. An herbaceous stem, or similar tissue, may be placed between the jaws of the object clamp of the microtome and held firmly in place by tightening the clamp screw. Thin tissues such as leaves are placed within split pith and the pith wedged and clamped in the microtome in the same manner. Textile fibers natural or chemical may be threaded together (as many as possible) in a thin needle and then drawn through a good fresh cork, the fibers are then left in the cork held closely together by it and supporting each other. In this way very satisfactory cross sections of textile fibers can be made and the thin cork section with the fibers in the middle can be put on a microscope slide. There are better methods for sectioning textile fibers * but the cork technique is still quite popular. A hand sectioning razor is used on the small microtomes or a regular microtome knife in the larger instruments. The stroke of the knife is a slicing motion. The surface of fresh plant tissue should be kept wet by adding a

* See bibliography.

FIGURE 52

Minot Precision microtome for large specimens.

drop of water to it between sections with a camel's hair brush. After three or four sections are on the knife they are taken off with the brush and placed in water in Stender of Syracuse dishes. They can then be put on the microscope slide by drawing it under them and thus picking them up. If necessary the proper staining techniques can be used and after mounting and covering with a cover glass they are ready for the microscope.

Celloidin Method—The celloidin method is preferred for large tissues and organs and for brittle and delicate materials. The celloidin is not removed from the tissues and holds the delicate structure permanently together. The material to be cut is embedded in one of the commercial celloidins (cellulose nitrate), the slow burning kinds are preferable. The disadvantages of this method are that the embedding time is long unless one of the special, rapid methods is used; the fact that serial sections cannot be cut and thus each section must be handled individually, and since it is not feasible to dissolve the embedding medium from the section only stains which do not stain celloidin may be used.

For materials not injured by moderate amounts of heat the rapid process (Walls, 1932) hurries infiltration and preparation of the tissue. The slower, cold method takes more time but it does not damage the tissue. It may take as long as six months or a year to embed a hemisphere of a brain or a whole lung and to harden it sufficiently for cutting. Naturally, smaller specimens can be prepared in much less time.

The chief difficulty in celloidin sectioning arises from trying to cut improperly prepared material. If the blocks are not adequately hardened they cannot be cut successfully. They should be dense enough to cut at the required thickness for if they are not sufficiently hard, the sections will be uneven and distorted. If the block is too hard irregularities may occur. *The surface of the block and the surface of the knife should be kept wet with 70% alcohol and as soon as the sections are removed they should be placed into alcohol.*

A slicing stroke is also used for celloidin sectioning (see position of knife in fig. 51). The declination or tilt of the knife, that is the angle at which it is set in a sliding microtome from a horizontal line will depend on the bevel of its cutting edge and the hardness of the tissue. It is convenient to let large sections roll up on the knife and then lifted off and unrolled into 70% alcohol.

The knife must be *very sharp* because any irregularities in the edge will leave marks on the section. The block and the materials for embedding must be kept free from dust because dust particles catching on the edge of the knife spoil the section. This is especially true when very thin sections are being cut. Silicious or calcareous material must be removed before sectioning.

The most common cause for irregularities in cutting is partial drying of the surface of the block. If it is necessary to stop cutting even for a short time the block should be covered with absorbent cotton and saturated with alcohol or else removed from the microtome and placed in alcohol.

The annoyance of keeping the block and knife wet with alcohol has led to the development of the dry process. After the tissue is embedded and hardened it is soaked in oil such as cedar oil which lubricates the block during cutting. As the sections are removed from the knife they are placed in the same oil. Such oil soaked blocks may be sectioned on regular rotary microtomes because no slicing stroke is necessary. The method has been found very satisfactory for making sections of difficult organs such as an entire eye.

Celloidin embedded blocks are sometimes embedded again in paraffin to hold them for sectioning.

The size and the thinness of the sections which may be cut depends on the size of the microtome and its general construction and condition, the sharpness and the declination of the knife *and the skill of the operator*. Only experienced, well trained microtomists can cut sections of two or three microns successfully and then only with an excellent microtome which is in perfect condition and with adequately embedded material. The inexperienced person should not attempt sections of less than 6 or 8 microns, preferably 8 or 10.

Paraffin Method—Blocks of material embedded in paraffin may be cut rapidly on a rotary microtome. Successive sections adhere to each other and form a ribbon (fig. 53) which facilitates handling and mounting the sections.

The objections to the paraffin method are the limitations due to the nature of paraffin itself and the possible injury to delicate tissues which may occur because of the high temperatures necessary during infiltration.

Different samples of paraffin have different melting points. Those with low melting points are more translucent and less brittle but compress more in sectioning. In warm rooms higher melting point paraffins must be used than in colder laboratories. It is also possible to condition the paraffin by the addition of various materials such as bayberry wax which improves its plasticity and cutting qualities. Certain waxes may be added to paraffin to harden it without increasing its melting point. *Thorough infiltration is important.* For critical work in some tissues it may be necessary to infiltrate in a vacuum to remove air from the specimen. For fine work it is necessary to match the hardness of the

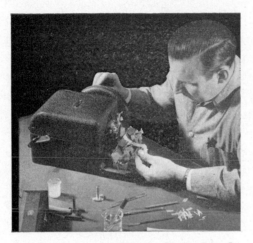

Courtesy Spencer Lens Co.

FIGURE 53

Large rotary precision microtome.

paraffin to the hardness of the tissue. The hardness of the tissue depends on its structure and the preparatory treatment (See Richards—The Effective Use and Proper Care of the Microtome, page 39).

Unless the hardness of the paraffin is adapted to the temperature at which the cutting is done and the nature of the tissue, good thin sections cannot be expected. This regardless of the excellence of the microtome and perfection of the knife. If the material has been properly dehydrated in the first place it is possible to reimbed it in another paraffin should the first prove unsatisfactory. Several changes of the melted paraffin should be used to wash out the former paraffin.

In actual cutting the knife should be set at 90 degrees to the direction of the cut (no slice angle) and tilted to as little clearance as will give good sections. This is true when cutting paraffin embedded materials either with the rotary or sliding microtomes. Here again it is useless to expect good sections if the knife is not in excellent condition and very sharp.

The block must be trimmed so that the edges parallel to the knife are straight and parallel to each other. If this is not done the ribbon will not be straight and the distortion will be increased. A camel's hair brush is used to handle the ribbon. It may be necessary to hold the first few sections on to the knife with gentle pressure of the brush until the ribbon forms. The ribbon is then raised with a dissecting needle and placed over the brush. It is then withdrawn from the knife with one hand as the ribbon lengthens while the flywheel of the microtome is being operated with the other hand. The desired lengths of ribbon are placed in order on smooth paper or in a shallow box until they are mounted on the slides.

Metal object holders (fig. 54) may be used to mount the specimen in the microtome. The holder is warmed enough to melt the paraffin. A hot spatula or knife is passed around the edges of the base of the block and it is then attached to the object holder and allowed to harden and cool thoroughly before actual cutting begins. Paraffin blocks (after heating their surfaces with a warm spatula) may also be attached to special fiber blocks or to wood blocks and then placed between the jaws of the object clamp of the microtome. Wood blocks are not as satisfactory if very fine even sections are desired because they cannot be held between the clamp jaws sufficiently rigidly without any "give." If metal object holders are not being used it is better to use the fiber blocks.

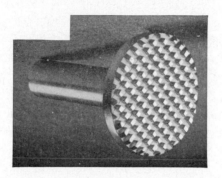

Courtesy Spencer Lens Co.

FIGURE 54

Object holder for paraffin blocks.

An air conditioned room maintained at the optimum temperature would be ideal for paraffin sectioning, but since few laboratories are so equipped the usual method for controlling the cutting temperature is as follows. The block is immersed in ice water, dried, placed on the microtome and cut before it warms up unduly. The knife also must be cold. Ice blocks are often used during cutting to keep the block and the knife cool. Various other adequate methods for temperature control have been published.

Rate of Cutting Speed for Various Types of Microtomes

In using rotary microtomes many technicians try to cut entirely too fast. This is wrong as the sections won't be as good and the microtome is placed under unnecessary strains which may be harmful in time. Some paraffin blocks of tissue must be cut slowly to obtain the best sections.* Others give a better ribbon if the microtome is run at a slightly greater speed. Take your time, work as fast as possible but without rushing. The motor drive of Spencer rotary microtomes should not be run faster than sixty cuts per minute, 40 or 50 is better in many cases.

Celloidin sections must necessarily be cut slowly with a firm steady motion of the slide block which holds the knife. No hesitation once the section has been begun.

Frozen sections also cut better slowly and also without hesitation.

Frozen Sections

Some materials may be placed directly on the freezing chamber of a freezing attachment for a microtome (fig. 50). They are then frozen and sectioned with little damage to the tissue. The disadvantage is that there is apt to be some distortion from both the freezing and the cutting. It is difficult to cut sections of more than ¾ of an inch square and considerable skill is required to obtain sections thinner than 15 microns. Usually frozen sections are cut at about 15 to 20 microns. CO_2 is generally used to freeze the sections.

The sample to be frozen should be trimmed to about ¾ of an inch square or less and 3 to 5 mm. thick. Place a few drops of water, or better of gum sugar, on the freezing chamber, place the tissue on it and add just enough fluid to surround it. Freeze the tissue

* Many experienced technicians use at times two or three different speeds when making one revolution of the flywheel.

slowly by turning on the CO^2 for a moment or two and turning it off. A series of successive jets freeze better and waste less gas than running it continuously. The tissue should be held fast against the chamber until

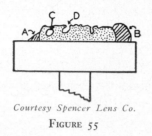

Courtesy Spencer Lens Co.

FIGURE 55

Diagram illustrating difficulties with freezing technique: (A)—Small wall of ice around object helps to hold it. (B)—Too much ice. (C and D) —Hard ice crystals which tear the specimen may form here.

freezing begins. When the block is about two thirds frozen, level off the top of the section and then complete the freezing. It is preferable to freeze the block a little harder than can be cut then as it warms up and reaches the right stage, make the required number of sections. If the block is frozen too hard the sections crumble, if it is too soft the tissues are injured and smeared together.

Here again the knife must be sharp and cool (there are special cooling devices for freezing microtomes) and set at the right tilt. With a cool knife and fast cutting, three or four sections may be cut and transferred at one time from the knife to the storage dish.

Figure 55 illustrates some difficulties in the freezing technique. Do not get too much water around the section and thus have a wall of ice around the specimen. If the tissue is spongy and is embedded only in water, hard ice crystals will form in places such as C and D and tear the tissue as the knife goes through it. Such tissues should at least be soaked for some time in gum sugar before freezing.

Rapid methods have been developed for hospital use as well as methods for staining, dehydrating and mounting frozen sections. These methods are covered in standard text books.

Importance of Proper Care of Microtomes

When one considers the fact that microtomes are instruments so precise that they are capable of cutting sections as fine as one or two microns, it is immediately obvious that they must be well cared for. If they are neglected when left unused for a time the cost of putting them back into good working order may be high. This is due to the fact that if the carefully fitted slideways become rusty the only remedy is to take the entire instrument apart for removal of the oxidation and then a complete refitting is necessary. Often complete new parts must be replaced.

The slideways should be cleaned with a soft cloth when cutting is finished or at the end of the day. All bearings and slideways must be properly oiled as indicated for the separate instruments. If one must sin it is better to have too much oil than not enough on all parts which require it. Do not use thick oils which gum up easily. A thin good oil such as pike oil which is free of paraffin is better. *Small pieces of embedding material should be removed from the instruments.* If put away for a time all slideways should be well oiled and bright parts greased with light vaseline then the entire instrument carefully wrapped and placed where it will be free from dust. When not in use microtomes should be covered or placed in a cabinet carefully.

The same is true of the knives. If put away for a time they should be well greased. Always keep a knife not in use in a case so that its edge will not be damaged.

How to Sharpen Microtome Knives

Regardless of how good a microtome we have and how well embedded is the material it is impossible to cut good sections *unless the knife is sharp* and in good condition. How is the knife sharpened? How can we tell when it is sharp? The following tested methods may be helpful.

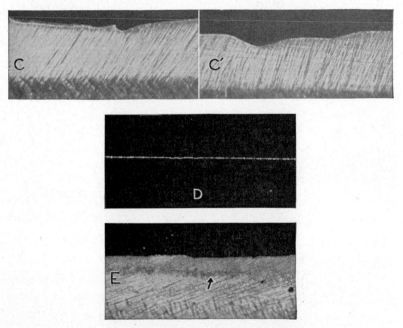

FIGURE 56

(C) Poor edge—nicks and rounded. (D) Wavy edge. (E) Edge burned at arrow from excessive stropping.

Most technicians apparently do not realize the importance of examining their knife with a microscope, hence they seldom really know when their knife is sharp. Also they sometimes strop a knife whether it needs it or not. If it does not need it and it is stropped the edge may be rounded and spoiled necessitating rehoning instead of being helped. Constant reference to the microscope is necessary during the sharpening process.

Let us assume that a new knife has been used for some time and we suspect that it is no longer as sharp as it should be. It is placed on the stage of a microscope with the edge pointing away from the operator, the back toward the operator. It is moved carefully so that its edge is just about over the center of the upper lens of the condenser of the microscope. A combination of light coming from the condenser and directly from a microscope lamp is used. The magnification should be about 100x (the 16 mm objective and the 10x ocular). If we place the microscope near a window and

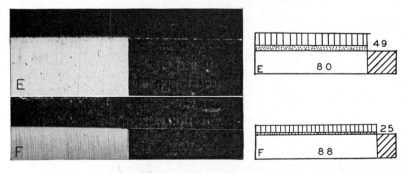

Courtesy Spencer Lens Co.

FIGURE 57

(E) Almost perfect. (F) Typical factory sharpened edge. (Diagrams illustrated next to edges show how compression decreases as edge quality improves.)

we use daylight for illuminating the knife from the bottom and a microscope lamp to illuminate it from the top we are ready to proceed. The light rays falling upon the surface of the knife should strike it at an

Courtesy Spencer Lens Co.

FIGURE 58

Microtome knife with back and handle for sharpening.

angle of about 25 to 40 degrees. Examine for nicks and for rounded edge. The light coming from the condenser will show us the nicks very clearly. If they are present they must be removed by honing and then a *little* stropping. We can tell if the edge is rounded by using the direct surface illumination from the microscope lamp. If we see a scratch which does not end in a nick at the very edge, it is probably rounded. The same is probably true if a dark shadow appears near the edge while the rest is bright because the reflection of the light rays is uneven. If we take a celluloid ruler and hold it pointed toward a window at a slight downward angle we get a good even reflection, if we bend it a little near the end a shadow appears because some light rays are not reflected toward our eyes. The same is true with a knife edge. If the edge is rounded a little honing and very slight stropping is also necessary.

If the edge appears free of nicks, perfectly straight, without deep scratches and without any signs of being rounded, it is O.K. If this is the case with the exception of *only one or two nicks* it is foolish to waste a great deal of time taking them out by honing; simply mark that part of the knife with a red pencil and use the rest of the knife edge for cutting until it is necessary to sharpen the major part of the knife.

Another method which some scientists consider better for observing the edge of a knife is to place it upon a wood support which holds it at an angle to the stage of the microscope, edge pointing upward and away from the operator. A strong beam of light is directed towards the edge from below and in front of the stage of the microscope. "D" in fig. 56 shows the result obtained with this method of lighting the edge of the knife.

How to Hone a Knife

In honing and stropping a knife the question is often asked "How many strokes should I use?" This cannot be answered definitely for there are many factors to be considered. The coarseness of the stone, the condition of the strop, the pressure exerted, the thickness of the soap solution on stone, etc. all determine the number of necessary strokes. The trial and error method must be used with constant reference to the microscope to avoid waste of labor and knife metal.

First Step: The yellow Belgian stone is generally considered best for the first step but at this writing due to war conditions it is difficult to obtain them. Mr. Tvestmann recommends that if a yellow Belgian stone is not available the thing to do is to get a fine grade carborondum stone,* originally designed to be used with oil to prevent chips of steel from the knife adhering to the stone. He has determined however that the

* Specially made by the Carborondum Company for this purpose and sold by many laboratory supply houses.

oil film over the stone makes it very difficult for an in-experienced person to know how much pressure to exert when honing. The stone will work very well, just like the Belgian stones, with soap and water but since the carborondum stone absorbs water like a sponge, Mr. Tvestmann recommends that it be first

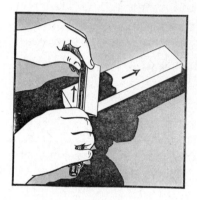 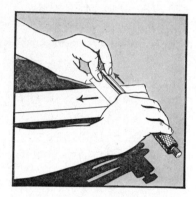

Courtesy Spencer Lens Co.

FIGURE 59

Honing the knife.

soaked in water for 5 or 10 minutes before using and then placed over a folded wet towel. The following holds for both the Belgian and the carborondum stones:

Take a wet towel folded four to six times and place it on the table. Put the stone on top of it. As honing proceeds the towel will give the stone a slight twisting movement which will partly neutralize the unavoidable uneven pressure generally exerted. Apply soap and water to the surface of the stone with a clean shaving brush. If the stone tends to give rough edge increase the soap which acts as a filler or, if this does not work, the surface may need treatment (explained later). In honing the thumb or fingers which will exert pressure should rest on the knife itself, not on the back—*The knife back must be in its proper position on the knife.* Each knife should have its own back. The strokes back and forth must be even and steady. One must feel that the stone is taking hold as the knife is moved across it with a slanting stroke from end to end. By referring to the microscope one can tell when the nicks have disappeared and the edge is straightening out. We can then go to the second step but before going into that let us see how to treat the surface of a stone if it is no longer in good condition:

Treatment of Stone Surface

The surface is treated with a piece of plate glass of about 2 x 3 inches. Place some water on the stone and move the glass plate back and forth across the entire surface with a rotary motion. The glass plate is held flat on the stone as this is done. This will take off all the sharp edges and smooth it out so it will be again in good condition. There is a big difference in the results before and after treatment if the stone has been used for some time. This treatment holds for both the yellow Belgian and the carborondum stones.

Second Step

The blue stone which has a finer grain than the Belgian or Carborondum is generally used for the second step. Sometimes however, it causes trouble because due to its characteristics it tends to collect metal chips from the knife which may cause nicks. Tvestmann recommends that no blue stone be used at all but instead to go directly from the first honing to a good horse leather strop mounted flat and tight on a board. Sprinkle on its surface *dry* some fine *white* polishing rouge as used by optical shops. The strop so treated takes the place of the blue stone without its drawbacks. Naturally if the strop is used the movement of the stroke is away from the edge of the knife instead of the reverse as on the stone. A slanting motion is also used keeping the back of the knife and the edge flat on the strop just the same as when a stone is used. *Never use a strop loose* hanging from a nail like barbers do. The edge of a microtome knife is not like that of a barber's razor. It must be infinitely better. If the strop is loose the edge will be rounded. After several strokes and again consulting the microscope we go to the final step.

Final Operation

We use another good strop mounted tight on a board, nothing whatever on it. This must be kept scrupulously clean. No hand should touch its surface just before

FIGURE 60A

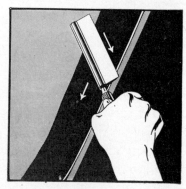

Courtesy Spencer Lens Co.

FIGURE 60B

Stropping the knife.

using it. The surface must not be too slippery and smooth, for if it is, it won't do any good but, on the contrary, it may round out the edge of the knife. It must offer a gentle but firm resistance to the knife as it is stroked along its surface. If surface is too smooth longer stropping is necessary and this is dangerous.

Usually it is better always to clean the strop before using it. Take a clean dry towel and clean its surface carefully with it. The knife should also be cleaned first with a little xylol. Don't forget the knife back, its surface should also be clean all around.

If the previous operations have been done properly only a few firm even strokes are necessary. Now we should have a good edge and the knife is ready for the microtome. First however, consult the microscope again and examine the edge as mentioned before.

The Glass Plate Method

The glass plate method is convenient, rapid and inexpensive. A piece of 3/16″, or thicker, plate glass 12 to 14″ long and at least an inch wider than the length of the knife should be provided. The abrasive should be purchased graded to size or prepared by making a suspension in water and settling it in a tall cylinder. The heavy particles rapidly fall to the bottom, while the lighter particles fall more slowly. After standing for a given time, determined from experiment, save the middle portion containing particles of proper size. For grinding an average size of 20 microns with none larger than 40 microns may be used. For final polishing of the facet, particles averaging 4 microns and less than 8 microns may be used. The particles should be suspended in a solution of neutral soap (about 1 per cent). To smooth the edge when nicks must be removed No.

303 or 304 Corundum may be used. Levigated alumina or No. 305s Corundum are suitable for ordinary sharpening and after the above grinding compounds. Diamantine or similar material should be used for the final polishing of the cutting facets.

The back and handle are attached to the knife in their proper positions. If the edge is not straight it is straightened by rubbing gently on a smooth stone holding the knife at right angles to the stone. The back and handle are used the same and the stroke is the same as when honing, except that the knife is pushed and pulled straight for nearly the length of the plate. As the plate is wider than the knife the diagonal stroke is unnecessary.

The finer abrasive is used for the final polishing and very little is required. The amounts used depend on the size and kind of abrasive, the rate of the stroke, the hardness and condition of the knife. A little practice soon teaches the proper proportions. Too much abrasive should be avoided. It is well to wash the plate free from abrasive occasionally to get rid of large particles and any bits of steel freed from the edge. The edge should be held evenly against the glass and not forced against it as the latter will round the edge rather than sharpen it. Any irregularity of the facets indicates uneven grinding or polishing. During the polishing operation fresh abrasives should be used from time to time and towards the end the abrasives should be more dilute than in the beginning. Watch the progress of sharpening and stop when the light reflected from the cutting edge becomes minimal. The facets should show a good polish under the microscope. If such a knife is well sharpened, stropping will not add further to its sharpening.

However, if the knife is not perfectly honed and is

slightly rough, stropping will assist in forming an edge. Stropping should not be overdone to give a curved edge.

How to Improve Surface of Strop When It Is Too Slippery and Shiny

Mr. Tvestmann assures us that the following method is very effective: Take a clean towel and moisten it with xylol. Use it to rub the surface of the strop well. Let the strop dry *thoroughly* for an hour or two. Take a dry piece of white soap and with it draw several criss crosses about ¾″ apart along the surface of the strop. Wash hands well and dry them thoroughly, then with the thumb spread these soap criss crosses over the entire surface of the strop working in the soap well for a few minutes. Leave the strop alone overnight and the moisture in the air, according to Mr. Tvestmann, will dissolve this fine film of soap and raise the fibres of the leather to give the necessary resistance to the knife. If the condition of the strop is very bad this operation may have to be repeated two or three times.

Trouble Shooting

Before one goes to the expense of asking for a repair man to inspect a microtome which is not giving satisfaction, or goes to the expense of shipping it to the factory for repair, it is well to try to determine first whether or not the microtome really needs repairs. The instrument may be perfect and still not give good results. As we have seen in the previous pages proper mounting is essential and we must first be sure that our material has been properly prepared for sectioning.

The New York Office of a large manufacturer of microtomes has kept records of "microtome trouble

calls." These records show the startling fact that 75%
of the trouble is "knife trouble." Either the knives are
not sharp (dull, rounded edges, etc.), or the tilt or declination at which they are being used is incorrect for
the bevels of their edge. 10% is usually due to poor
embedding and *only* 15% of the cases on record required repairs to the instrument. Other manufacturers
have had more or less the same experience, therefore
the recommended procedure for trouble shooting is as
follows:

1. Inspect knife edge carefully with the microscope
as described previously under "How to Sharpen
Knives." If the edge is perfect and we are pretty sure
that the mounting is O.K. then the trouble is probably
the tilt at which the knife is set. If the knife is not
sharp or if the edge is rounded, sharpen the knife until
its edge is perfect.

2. Check the tilt (sometimes called declination) of
the knife. It is difficult to set down a definite rule for
the proper tilt but what follows is helpful in the majority of cases for generally the knife is put on the
knife holder with either too much or not enough tilt
to it in relation to the block which is going to be cut.

The proper tilt is determined for rotary microtomes
in this manner: Place the knife in either clamp of the
knife holder tilted toward the specimen, but leaving
part of it extended at the side. Place on this extended
part the knife back. Take a straight ruler or a pencil
and hold it perfectly straight in a vertical position
against the knife edge near its end. Rotate the knife
keeping its edge in contact with the pencil to a point
where there is a space of about ⅛ of an inch between
the knife back and the pencil. With a fairly new knife

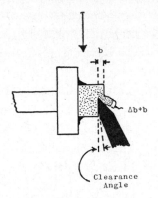

FIGURE 61

Correct tilt of knife.

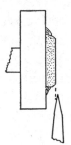

FIGURE 62

Not enough tilt--wedging effect.

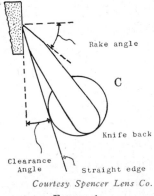

FIGURE 63

Too much tilt.

this is usually the right tilt. The back is taken off and the knife secured firmly in the clamps at this declination. If the knife has been worn down some by honing and stropping, the bevels at its edge will probably make a larger angle and consequently the tilt must be increased a little. The space between the back and the vertical pencil should then be about 3/16 of an inch. Avoid going beyond this for if the tilt is greater we would not cut but scrape. If the tilt is not enough the knife will exert a wedge effect on the block which is just as bad. Both obviously cause uneven thickness of sections. The tilt must be just right for perfect sectioning.

In sliding microtomes the tilt is determined in the same manner but the pencil naturally is held in a horizontal position away from the edge of the knife instead of vertical. An experienced microtomist can sometimes look at a knife and put it at its right tilt without any measurements but this is rather the exception than the rule. If not sure measure as above.

3. If after checking one and two the trouble persists then check the microtome itself. First the knife clamps in the knife holder. Do they rotate freely within their sockets so that the proper tilt can be reached? Is there any paraffin or oil under the holder which may prevent its being held immovable where it is placed? Make sure that the bottom surface of the holder is free of oil or paraffin and the same is true of the upper surface of the main base of the microtome on which the knife holder rests. These surfaces must be kept clean. If this is not done the thickness of the sections may vary. Check moving parts for wear and lost motion. If the slideways are loose repairs are definitely necessary. The same is true of the feeding mechanism. Make sure that

the pawl engages the predetermined number of teeth on the ratchet wheel and that it falls each time right between two teeth not on top of one or another. This will also cause skipping and eventually will damage the expensive ratchet wheel.

Are the slideways gummed up with thick oil? Heavy oil will tend to gum bearing surfaces and the machine will work sluggishly. This is due to the fact that bearing surfaces are fitted so closely that they will permit only the use of thin oil.

4. If none of the above mentioned three causes of trouble are found then we can be quite sure that it is improper embedding. For this we must refer our readers to the embedding techniques in the text books and to Dr. Richard's booklet on the microtome.

Before closing this "trouble section" it is well to mention that lost motion can be found on microtomes which do not have the feeding mechanism independent of the forward movement of the object in the following manner. Hold object clamp with either hand. On sliding microtomes, other than the inclined plane type, exert an up and down pressure on the object clamp and see if it moves up and down. There should be no such motion. It should not move. If it does there is lost motion which causes skipping. This should be corrected by a qualified repair man. On rotary microtomes of *this same type* the same can be ascertained by checking if there is a forward and back motion of the object (since the object moves horizontally instead of vertically) when some pressure is exerted. Don't overdo this test, a slight firm pressure is all that is necessary.

How to Use Entire Length of Knife on a Rotary Microtome

Place pencil across the bottom of the two knife clamps in the knife holder. Insert knife in one knife holder just far enough so that its end will engage the specimen. In this way the ends of the knife can be used for trimming and by pushing the knife toward the other clamp a little at a time its entire length can eventually be used. This has been tested and proven very satisfactory and practical. The pencil acts as a good support for the part of the knife which is not resting on a clamp. Not recommended for very thin sections with hard material but good for routine work.

Razor Blade Holders

Razor blades, especially the flat thicker types of safety razor blades can be used quite well for microtome sectioning. This provided the holder is properly designed. Many are not. With a good holder which holds the blade right up to the edge and in fact becomes with it almost a complete microtome knife good work can be done. These are used in large beginning classes in technique to avoid damage to microtome knives. Also for cutting materials where the edge is rapidly destroyed. As soon as the edge is worn, a new blade should be used. Generally the razor blade holder is not as efficient as a real microtome knife. Exceptionally good technicians however have been known to cut very thin sections with these holders and good blades. It is better for the average person not to attempt to cut less than 8 microns with a razor blade holder, and 10 would be better. Mainly used for paraffin sectioning.

Courtesy Spencer Lens Co.

FIGURE 64

Razor blade holder.

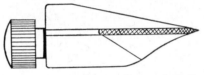

Courtesy Spencer Lens Co.

FIGURE 65

Proper position of blade in holder—blade and inside surfaces
of holder must be free of paraffin.

A Check List of Difficulties Commonly Encountered in Section Cutting *

Celloidin Embedded Material

The knife should slice through the material with a
slant angle of about 10°–35° to the direction of the
cut and the knife should be tilted more than required
for paraffin imbedded material.

1. The chief difficulty comes from trying to cut improperly prepared material. Adequate impregna-
   tion of a large organ like a hemisphere of a brain
   may take a year. Improperly hardened blocks can-

---

* "The Effective Use and Proper Care of the Microtome"—Richards;
Spencer Lens Co.

not be sectioned successfully. Pressure methods involving heat speed up the process and are available when warming will not injure the material.

2. Lengthwise scratches or splits in the section may be due to:

   a. Nicks in the knife—use a different part of knife or resharpen.

   b. Particles of hard material in the block.

      i. Dust or dirt in the celluloidin stock solution —let stand and use only upper portion after the particles have settled out or filter the stock solution.

      ii. Calcareous or silicious deposits in the material —decalcify or desilicify.

3. Specimen falls out of section, is mushy and soft.

   a. Dehydration was incomplete.

   b. Infiltration incomplete—reinfilter, reimbed and harden.

   c. Harden block if too soft, in chloroform, or a mixture of equal parts of 95% alcohol and glycerine.

4. Variation in thickness of sections.

   a. Loose screws on knife or block holders—tighten all set screws.

   b. Knife holder depressed or raised by the hand while sectioning—hold knife block so as not to move it vertically while cutting.

   c. Knife not tilted enough to clear facet of cutting bevel.

   d. Knife too dull.

   e. Microtome worn and out of adjustment.

   f. Material not hardened properly.

   g. Slight drying of block between sections.

Paraffin Embedded Material

1. Ribbon fails to form.
   a. Room is too cold or paraffin too hard.
      i.   Use softer (lower melting point) paraffin.
      ii. Warm knife slightly by blowing the breath on it, or immersing in *warm* (not hot) water.
      iii. Place a desk lamp so that the light and heat fall on the knife and block.
   b. Tilt the knife less.
   c. Cut thinner sections.
   d. Knife may be too dull—resharpen.
   e. Dip block into a softer paraffin and trim so that a thin layer remains on the upper and lower edge of the block.
   f. Unroll the section and hold it lightly against the knife with a camel's hair brush. If the first few sections can be held down, the ribbon will often form and follow.
2. Crooked ribbons.
   a. When sections are wedge shaped the sides of the block are not trimmed parallel.
   b. Edge of block not parallel to knife edge.
   c. Try another part of the knife—sometimes irregularities of the knife edge cause crooked ribbons.
   d. The paraffin at one side of the block may be softer than at the other side, especially if the material has been reimbedded in a paraffin of different hardness—reimbed the material and stir the melted paraffin.
3. Sections compressed, wrinkled and jammed together.
   a. Knife too dull.

b. Room too warm—cool trimmed block and knife in very cold or ice water immediately before sectioning, or reimbed in a harder paraffin.

c. Knife tilt too slight so facet bevel rubs over block —increase tilt.

d. Knife edge gummed with paraffin—wipe with finger or cotton moistened with xylene.

e. Soak block in water from an hour or two to over night, before cutting.

f. Cutting too rapidly—very thin sections should be cut slowly.

4. Sections crumble and specimen may tear out.

a. Material incompletely dehydrated or not properly cleared.

b. When soft and mushy, material incompletely infiltered—reinfilter and imbed. (Salvage rarely possible if material was incompletely dehydrated.)

c. Alcohol not completely removed by clearing fluid.

d. Object too long in paraffin bath or paraffin too hot.

e. Subject hard and brittle due to clearing fluid. Try toluene in place of xylene or a mixture of toluene and cedar oil.

f. Try celluloidin imbedding, or a rubber or asphalt mixture with paraffin for fragile material.

g. Try dioxan method for dehydrating.

5. Split ribbon or lengthwise scratches in ribbon.

a. Due to nicks in knife—use another part of knife or resharpen knife.

b. Use less tilt of knife so it will cut rather than scraping.

   c. Knife edge dirty.

   d. Object may be too large for paraffin method—
use celloidin.

   e. Hard particles in block may cause scratching.

      i. Dirt in paraffin—filter or decant melted par-
affin.

     ii. Crystals from killing fluid (mercuric chlo-
ride) when washing was insufficient.

    iii. Calcareous or silicious particles in materials
—decalcify or desilicify.

6. Knife rings on up stroke and sections are scratched.

   a. Change knife tilt to greater or less degree—tilt
must be sufficient to clear facet bevel, but not
enough to scrape instead of cut.

   b. Material is too hard.

      i. Soak in water to soften.

     ii. Clearing may be at fault.

   c. A thicker or wedge shaped knife may prevent
springing of the edge when cutting.

   d. Material may be too tough for paraffin method
—try celluloidin.

7. Sections lifted from knife on up stroke.

   a. Increase knife tilt.

   b. Room too warm or paraffin too soft—try harder
paraffin—cooler room; or cool block.

   c. Knife may be dull—resharpen.

8. Sections stick to knife.

   a. Knife edge dirty.

   b. Increase knife tilt.

   c. Try a sharper knife.

9. Undulations in the surface of the section.

   a. Tighten all set screws on knife and block holders
and see that knife holder is clamped fast to microtome base.

    b. Lessen excessive knift tilt to prevent vibration.

10. Scratching noise during cutting.

    a. Material may be too hard, or small regions of material may be hard.

11. Sections fly and stick to parts of microtome or other nearby objects, due to static electricity formed from the friction of cutting. This usually occurs only in winter when the air is very dry.

    a. Increase humidity of room by boiling water in an open pan, or burn a bunsen burner in the room.

    b. Ground microtome to a water pipe with a wire or a chain.

    c. Ionize the air by an electrical method.

12. Sections vary in thickness or are skipped.

    a. Knife not tilted enough to clear facet or bevel, or tilted too much, and tissue is compressed until the inevitable expansion gives a thick section.

    b. Some of the clamping set screws on the block or knife holder are not tight or knife holder block not clamped firmly.

    c. Microtome worn through lack of lubrication, or not in adjustment.

    d. Very large blocks or blocks with hard regions may spring knife edge while sectioning—soak block in water to soften, use other methods for softening the material or imbed in celluloidin. The block will soak quicker if the paraffin is trimmed off one side to expose the tissue. Very little water is absorbed, but this process sometimes makes possible cutting hard or tough material.

Frozen Section Technique

Fresh material may be cut as soon as frozen, but better sections may be obtained after the tissue has been killed, washed and soaked in a gum syrup. Tissue fragments may be mounted in gelatin before cutting. Material in alcohol should be passed through a series of alcohols to water and fixed tissues should be washed before freezing.

Freeze with moderately rapid gas flow. A small glass tumbler with an opening about the diameter of the freezing head may be held over the tissue while freezing to aid in even hardening.

Test cutting conditions and when the tissue has reached the right hardness cut the required number of sections quickly with an even and slow stroke. It may be convenient to freeze the material hard and cut when it has thawed to the right stage.

The knife must be cooled to prevent the sections sticking to it. Sections may be removed with a camel's hair brush and placed into distilled water. When using a chisel shaped blade, hold it against the chest or body to brace the arms and make the cut by swaying the body.

Very hard or dense tissues may not be cut at less than 18–20 μ. The average thickness is often 15 μ. Considerable skill is required for cutting thinner sections.

All set screws holding the freezing equipment and knife must be tight to avoid vibration when cutting frozen sections.

CHAPTER V

THE USE AND CARE OF THE MICROSCOPE

Preparation of Materials

THERE are very few materials which can be examined with a high power microscope exactly as they occur in nature for they must be thin enough to transmit sufficient light and not so thick that the details are obscured. Since some specimens are not sufficiently transparent, only their surface can be examined unless it is possible to prepare them in some way that will enable us to see through them. There are many methods for the preparation of materials. These various methods have been evolved through the years to solve particular problems and obviously the exact explanation of these techniques is not within the scope of this book. For specific methods we must refer our readers to the bibliography at the end of the book. Here we can only treat the subject in a very general way. Sufficient only to give the student some basic knowledge of the problem.

Dry preparations have very limited possibilities for microscope examination under high powers. *They are usually examined with low magnifications,* preferably with the low power stereoscopic binocular microscopes. It is possible however to use the conventional monobjective microscopes if the magnifications used do not go beyond 100 or 150 diameters. There are a few exceptions to this however. Diatomes for example may be mounted dry on a slide under a cover glass to take advantage of the difference in refractive index between them and air. Also, small microorganisms such as bacteria may be smeared on a slide, allowed to dry and examined with or without staining. Metal surfaces and minerals after proper polishing and preparation also are usually examined dry. However, we cannot take a leaf from a tree, or a fly or a spider and expect to see its details *under high magnification* unless we first prepare such materials properly.

Many *temporary preparations* reveal more detail after mounting in a drop of water and covering them with a thin cover glass. The cover glass is necessary to prevent the liquid from getting onto the surface of the objective and also to give a flat surface to the material so that the light enters the objective as shown in fig. 66. Since water sometimes evaporates rapidly, if other fluids, like glycerine, will not injure the specimen, it is better to use such a fluid instead of water. If water must be used it is helpful to add a drop of water to the edge of the cover glass from time to time to replace that lost by evaporation. This prevents the possible crushing of a delicate specimen by the cover glass as it is drawn down toward the slide by the evaporation of the water.

Permanent preparations are made by mounting the specimen in a transparent material and then covering it carefully with a cover glass of the proper thickness. This procedure *requires the dehydration* of the specimen with alcohol, dioxan, or other suitable chemical. After it has been carefully dehydrated it is mounted in Canada Balsam or Gum Damar, the cover glass is then placed over it carefully and the slide allowed to dry slowly. When properly labeled and carefully stored these preparations will last for many years and they can be referred to at any time. Canada Balsam may be slightly acid which may fade the dyes used to stain the specimen (if it is stained), therefore synthetic resins are replacing Canada Balsam for mounting to a considerable extent. If there is danger that completely dehydrating the specimen would damage it unduly, it may be mounted in glycerine jelly, without complete dehydration.

If we have a mass of material from which we want to select certain specimens for examination this can be done by means of forceps, or if in a liquid preparation, by means of a capillary pipette. Such a pipette can be made by using an ordinary medicine dropper and drawing out its tip in a hot flame. If a bit of plant or animal tissue is placed in a drop of water it may be *teased* apart by means of two dissecting needles until some of the parts are separate and thin enough for examination under a microscope. Harder materials are sometimes prepared by crushing them and then sifting out the parts desired. Another form of separation is to place the material in a bag of cloth and to knead it under water so that the parts not desired will separate out and wash away.

Sedimentation is another common method for separation of materials. We can take our mixture and suspend it in water or some other liquid and allow it to settle slowly. The coarser and heavier particles settle more rapidly than the finer particles, thus by taking samples at various depths within the column of water, or at different times, it is frequently possible to get the specimens we want for examination. This method, as well as sifting through different sizes of mesh, is often used for abrasives or for soils.

There is also *selective solubility* with various chemicals. This is a convenient method for removing material not desired, i.e., cloth may be treated with alkali to dissolve the wool and leave the cotton fibre so that the proportion of the two materials may be estimated. Oils or other solvents are sometimes used as mounting media to *clear* the material not desired. For instance, in studying adulteration, mounting in paraffin or clove oil may make the starch transparent so that crystals or other materials present may be seen.

As we have seen in the previous chapter many specimens must be sectioned with microtomes before a proper examination can be made. Hard materials, like rocks and metals, have to be sectioned with a diamond saw or other type of cutting machine, then ground down to the necessary thinness and polished before or after they have been mounted on a slide depending on the material. Metal surfaces may require chemical etching to reveal their characteristic details. We shall go into this more extensively in Chapter VII under "Metallurgical Microscopes."

It is quite apparent that the skillful preparation of materials is of fundamental importance. If a specimen is badly prepared the most expert microscopist, using the finest microscope, may not be able to identify it or see its structure. Learning the technique of preparing materials requires practice and usually the making and correcting all possible mistakes at least once. It is a field in which skill increases with practice and the beginner should not feel discouraged if at first he is not entirely successful. While up to a point it is possible to learn technique from books, it is easier and a shorter process to learn by watching a skilled person and from study under qualified supervision. If a person is not willing to take the time to learn the proper technique for the preparation of the particular type of specimens he wishes to study, then it is necessary to purchase prepared slides or to employ a skilled technician to do the preparatory work, for we must repeat that many specimens cannot be properly studied under high magnifications unless they are carefully and properly prepared first.

Preparations of Materials for Specialized Microscopes

Practical hints for the preparation of materials which are usually examined with a specialized microscope (such as stereoscopic, metallurgical and polarizing) will be found in the Chapters dealing with such microscopes, i.e., polishing of metal specimens in Chapter VII; rock sections Chapter VIII.

An Actual Example of the Proper Use of a Monobjective Compound Microscope

We have seen the importance of the preparation of the specimen, now let us take a properly prepared specimen and study it with a microscope. We shall *not* take any particular type of specimen for this example or attempt to interpret what we see. Here we are primarily interested in *how* to use the microscope to study our slide. This will also serve as a review of the previous chapters. Let us assume that our specimen is mounted on a standard 3 x 1 inch microscope slide, it has been properly stained and covered with a coverglass of the correct thickness for our objectives. This specimen is transparent and has many fine details in its structure

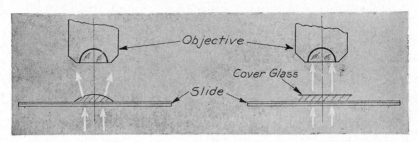

FIGURE 66

A cover glass should be used for best results.

which we want to study, but we also wish to study it as a whole, that is, first we want to see its general shape, and then the details of its finer structure. Such a study will require the use of several objectives and oculars in order to cover the various necessary magnifications. We shall use a good binocular microscope with a lamp like fig. 34 which we can prepare for various types of illumination.

Our microscope is equipped with a revolving nose-piece for four objectives (a quadruple nosepiece), and a condenser. The following objectives will be used: a 40mm 2.8X; a 16mm 10X; a 4mm 44X; and an oil immersion objective 1.8mm 95X. All the objectives are the regular achromatic lenses. Thus with the 10X oculars which we shall use, we are going to get magnifications of 28X, 100X, 440X and 950X. We also know that the lower the magnification the larger the field we can see, so to study the shape of the object which we want to see first as a whole we are going to use the lowest magnification.

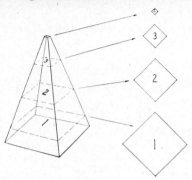

FIGURE 67

Depth is seen as successive layers.

The same technique is used if our microscope is a monocular instead of a binocular, the only difference is that in that case, we would not need as much light and we would not have to think of the interpupillary distance of the ocular tubes. On the other hand we would not be as comfortable during our observations.

We place our lamp in front of our microscope mirror (with its diaphragm opened wide) about 8 or 10 inches away and we place in the filter holder of the lamp both the ground glass and the clear blue glass filters. The slide is placed on the stage or on the mechanical stage of the microscope. We unscrew the top lens of the condenser so that the large field of the 40mm objective will be properly illuminated and it is swung to its working position. The light of the lamp is directed toward the center of the plane surface of the microscope mirror. Using the rack and pinion coarse adjustment we move the objective to a point about an inch and a half away

from the object and we place our head over the microscope so that our eyes are directly over the oculars,
almost touching them, two or three millimeters away
from their top lenses. Looking down through the ocu-

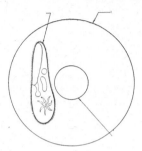

Courtesy Spencer Lens Co.

FIGURE 68

Incorrectly centered object not in field of higher power objective.

lars we move the mirror a little one way or the other so
that the field of view is evenly illuminated and we
focus first with the coarse adjustment and then with
the fine adjustment until the object comes into plain
view. Now we check our interpupillary distance carefully moving the ocular tubes from side to side slowly
until we get their separation exactly right so that the
right and left images blend perfectly and our eyes feel
comfortable and relaxed. We must make sure now that
we are seeing our specimen properly so we check our
light by making sure that the mirror is at its best position and that the back lens of the objective is filled with
light without any superfluous rays. We check this by
closing the iris diaphragm of the condenser until it coincides with the margin of the lens. This can be seen by
taking off an ocular and looking down the tube. If we
still have too much light we place neutral tint filters
between our lamp and the mirror of the microscope

until we get exactly the right amount of light which
suits our eyes. Never use more light than necessary.
If now by closing one eye first and then the other we
see our specimen perfectly clearly with *both* eyes well
and good, if not, we close the left eye first and focus
with the *fine adjustment* for the right eye. We then
leave the fine adjustment alone and focus for the left
eye with the focusing adjustment on the left ocular
tube of our binocular body. If this adjustment is on
the right tube of our microscope the procedure is reversed of course. Usually this individual focusing of
the eyes is necessary for few people's eyes focus exactly
the same. If we have done all the foregoing properly
our specimen can now be studied in comfort and can
be seen perfectly illuminated and clearly.

We find a particular section of the specimen that we
want to study with greater detail, that is with a higher
magnification. We move the slide so that that spot is
in the center of the field and we screw on to the condenser again its top element so that it is now complete
with all its lenses. We then raise it to its highest position so that it is almost touching the bottom of the slide.
The 16mm objective is rotated to its working position
and focused down with the coarse adjustment to a point
about 5mm (about ¼ of an inch) away from the object. It is now focused carefully with the coarse and
the fine adjustments until the object can be seen perfectly clearly. We must now open the iris of the condenser a little checking this as before because the N.A.
or the 16mm objective is greater and we need a cone of
light with a slightly larger angle. Now we can see
clearly that section of the specimen and details are revealed which could not be seen before.

Let us suppose that again we find a section of the field which appears to promise some interesting details which we must magnify still more in order for us to see them clearly. We swing our 4mm objective to its working position after having centered the spot which interests us in the middle of the field. If our objectives are "parfocal" only a slight focusing with the fine adjustment will be necessary and the spot will be somewhere in the field, if the objectives of our microscope are also "precentered," as is the case with most modern instruments. Again we must open the iris of the condenser to equalize our N.A. We can check this as before by taking off the ocular and looking down the

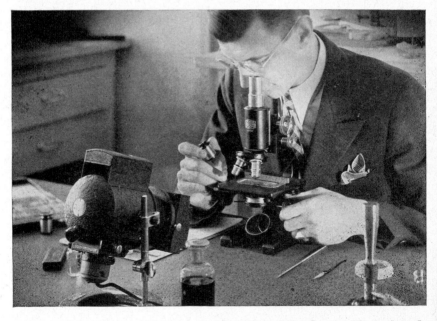

Courtesy Spencer Lens Co.

FIGURE 69

By looking down the tube after removing the ocular the back lens of
the objective can be observed to see if it is filled with light.

tube or if our condenser is graduated we set the lever
at a point where it coincides with the N.A. of our 4mm
objective. Now however, it is possible that we need
more light. Since we do not want to spoil our image
by opening the iris of the condenser beyond its proper
point, we simply remove one or two of the neutral tint
filters that we had placed before between the lamp and
the mirror of the microscope. The specimen can now
be seen properly and we can study its minute details.
We want to be surer about our light however so we
close the iris of the lamp to give us a circle of light of
about ½ inch to 1 inch in diameter. Now we can be
very sure that if the back lens of our objective is well
filled with light, we have a close approximation to
critical illumination. Perhaps this improves the results
a little for we may have disposed thus of some superfluous light rays but if we are very particular and really
want to be sure of seeing all that can be revealed by
our lens we try Köhler illumination before going to the
oil immersion lens and the highest possible magnifications.

Köhler illumination was described in Chapter III but
since it is important we shall review it here. We take
all the filters off the lamp, especially the ground glass
filter, and close the iris of the microscope condenser all
the way so that we can focus upon it the filaments of
the bulb in our lamp. We make sure that the center
filaments of our bulb are right in the center of our iris
and we put the *clear blue* glass back on the lamp. Since
by taking off the ground glass we are increasing the
light very materially, we place some neutral tint filters
between the lamp and the mirror of our microscope.
The iris of the microscope condenser is now opened to

its proper N.A. again and the iris of the lamp closed as far as it will go. We manipulate our mirror so the field is brilliantly illuminated and we focus the iris *of the lamp* upon our object *with the condenser of the microscope*. The object and the iris diaphragm of the lamp can now be seen at the same time. The iris of the lamp is opened until it just disappears from view. Now if the back lens of our objective is properly filled with light the object will be seen with surprising and beautiful clarity. We now check the proper combination of neutral tint filters so that exactly the right amount of light reaches our eyes.

It is time to examine our object with the highest magnifications our instrument can give us in order to see its most minute details. The use of the oil immer-

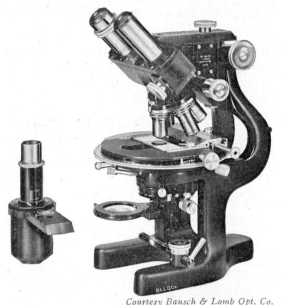

Courtesy Bausch & Lomb Opt. Co.

FIGURE 70

A research microscope of the reversed arm type.

sion lens is now necessary. If this is not done carefully there is danger of damaging our specimen and our lens. Also there's the possibility that the image will not be perfect. On the other hand if it is used correctly we are going to reach the limit of resolution of our optical system. Naturally the field of view is going to be greatly reduced and probably not all of the field is going to be in focus at one time. We must focus *with the fine adjustment* for the particular point we wish to study and move that point to the very center of the field. Also quite possibly, if we use 20X oculars which often have a diaphragm which reduces the size of the field materially this difference in focus will not be as apparent. As previously indicated this is not necessarily a defect of the lens for the oil immersion objectives of high apertures are not primarily designed to give a flat field but rather to give the best possible resolution of the object under observation.

Since it is probable that we have placed in the center of the field of the 4mm objective the particular part of the object we want to study, we are not going to touch the slide. The condenser is lowered a little so that a large drop of oil can be placed upon its top lens and then raised again until there's a good oil contact free of air bubbles between the top lens of the condenser and the under side of the slide. (This operation can be eliminated if we are going to be satisfied with a numerical aperture of about 1.00, but then the objective cannot give us its maximum resolution.) The illumination is checked again to make sure it is right as it was before. Now we put a drop of immersion oil on top of the cover glass and the immersion lens is swung into position. Before doing this it is better to raise the tube

with the coarse adjustment. The objective is now
lowered with the coarse adjustment *while we watch
this from the side* until there is a good oil contact between the front lens of the objective and the cover glass.
Now we can look through the oculars again and *with*

Courtesy E. Leitz, Inc

FIGURE 71

Leitz inverted microscope for use with a micromanipulator. (Note that
the objectives are *under* the stage and the condenser *above* the stage.)

the fine adjustment, never with the coarse, we get the
exact focus. The light is checked again, perhaps the
mirror needs a little adjustment or the condenser may
have to be raised or lowered somewhat. The iris of
the condenser is opened to match the N.A. of the objective and that of the lamp closed as far as possible.
The amount of light is again controlled with neutral
tint filters. If all this has been done properly and there
are no air bubbles in the oil (these can be seen by taking out the ocular and looking down the tube) the
finest details of our object can now be seen. We can
change the 10X huyghenian oculars and put in their
place 15X or 20X compensating oculars to give us the
greatest possible magnifications but we must remember
the "empty magnification" rule discussed in Chapter
II. It is better not to go beyond 1,000 times the numerical aperture of our objective and it is still better in
most cases to stay within 750 times of this N.A. As
we increase magnification we probably will want to
increase our light and we do this by eliminating one or
more of the neutral tint filters.

The first time that an oil immersion objective is used
it is difficult to focus it and to find the object but with
a little care and practice it can be done very quickly
and easily.

If *apochromatic objectives* are used instead of the
usual achromatics, let us remember that compensating
oculars must be used with them, preferably of the same
make as the objectives. Also, and this is important, the
high power *dry* apochromatic objectives have a correction collar to compensate for the cover glass thickness
to which they are so sensitive. For best results this
collar *must be used.* It's a little tricky at first but with

a little practice one can work the collar with one hand and the fine adjustment of the microscope with the other and thus reach optimum results. The only alternative is to measure the cover glass thickness and adjust the correction collar of the objective to that point.

The Use of Eyeglasses When Working with a Microscope

Many persons who regularly use spectacles often wonder if they can do without them when using the microscope. If they are near sighted or far sighted and have very little or no astigmatism, the answer is yes, they can use the microscope perfectly well without their glasses. The only trouble is that if the person is very near sighted or far sighted, and he must look away from the microscope to make a note, look up a reference, etc., then he must put on his glasses again. When he goes back to the microscope he removes them and so on which is naturally very annoying. Such persons therefore should accustom themselves to use their spectacles when working with the microscope. A person with a definite astigmatic condition always must use his eyeglasses with his microscope. If doubtful about this it is better to consult a good oculist.

If glasses are used with the microscope it is a good idea to put a rubber band or some other soft material around the mount of the ocular which holds the top lens of the eyepiece. This protects the eyeglasses from being scratched by the metal mount of the ocular.

It is also possible to attach to the top of the ocular an additional lens which has been ground to the prescription necessary for the worker, but in that case one must remember to use the proper ocular so equipped

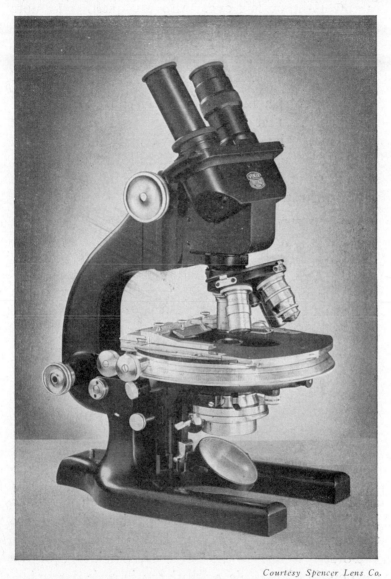

FIGURE 72

Research microscope with circular graduated mechanical stage.

145

for the right or left eye. Also the question of note making, etc. is always present.

How to Read a Vernier and Its Use on a Mechanical Stage

A vernier is a means of making linear or angular measurements that are more accurate than would be possible with the unaided eye. Verniers in microscopic apparatus are usually constructed to read in tenths of a millimeter, or if in angular measurements, degrees and minutes of rotation.

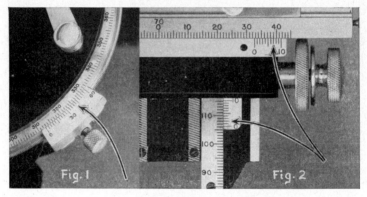

Courtesy Spencer Lens Co.

FIGURE 72A

Verniers in mechanical stages.

The vernier scale in Fig. 2 of cut 72A is only as long as nine graduations of the main scale which is divided in millimeters, even although the vernier is divided into ten equal parts and reads from one to ten.

To read a vernier the point of coincidence of the zero on the short scale, with the main scale determines the whole number, that is, the number to the *left* of the decimal point. Always read the lower whole number on the main scale to the left of the zero on the vernier. The only exception to this is when the zero line of the vernier exactly coincides with the whole number of the main scale in which case that is the number noted with no decimals after it. The point of coincidence of the line of the vernier scale which perfectly meets any line on the main scale is the decimal or tenth part of the millimeter.

In Fig. 2 of cut 72A therefore, the transverse, or so called, horizontal graduation reads 32.7mm. The reading on the to and from vernier or the so called, vertical scale is 106.2mm. If we were using a microscope and our mechanical stage gave us these readings at one particular position of the slide, we would know that a slide so marked when put back in exactly the same position would again show us the same part of the object. Thus, supposing we found a particular part of an object in our slide which we would like to study later with more care or to photograph it, then we would put a label on the slide reading: vert. 106.2, hor. 32.7, or as is often the custom, 106.2 by 32.7 writing down first the vertical and then the horizontal reading. Obviously this saves a great deal of searching time when referring back to a particular slide.

The reading of a circular vernier is very much the same except that one usually reads it in degrees and minutes of arc, each unit on the vernier scale representing so many minutes of arc. In the vernier shown in fig. 1, cut 72A which is graduated to 3 minutes of arc for each graduation the reading would be 312 degrees, 42 minutes, for the point of coincidence shown by the arrow on the vernier reads 42 (each graduation being equal to 3).

Drawings and Measurements by Projection

At times it is desirable to use this method for drawing and measuring. It is practical only if the material used is dry, that is the specimen must be a prepared slide with the material attached to it and preferably with a cover glass. It is better not to use this method when oil immersion lenses are necessary but for dry objectives it is perfectly practical with a monocular microscope.

Using the inclination joint of the microscope the tube is put in a horizontal position parallel to the table on which we are working. This of course puts the stage of the microscope in a vertical position and hence the objection to wet preparations and oil immersion.

A small rectangular prism is put over the ocular of the microscope with its diagonal surface up. (Many manufacturers sell these prisms properly mounted so that they can be easily attached.) The mirror of the microscope is removed. A beam of light from a powerful microscope lamp is directed in a straight line to the condenser. No ground glass is used in the lamp of course for this cuts down the light and we need all we can get. The objective used is focused on the object in the regular way with the coarse and fine adjustment. If the light is properly directed and controlled by focusing the condenser, and if we put a piece of paper under the prism we can see the image of the object greatly magnified on the paper. The magnification increases as the distance between the prism and the paper is increased, therefore if we place our projection unit (the microscope, prism and lamp) on a little table on top of the main table so that the distance from the prism to the paper is about 10 inches, then we shall see the image of the object magnified on the paper to about the same extent as we would see it with the eye on the microscope. If the distance is less than 10 inches the magnification is less, if more than 10 inches it will be more.* This can be easily checked by using a stage micrometer slide as our object (Chapter IX Accessories) and measuring with a regular ruler its magnified image on the paper. The ease with which measurements of an object can be made by this method will be immediately apparent for if we find that 1mm in our object slide equals 100mm on the paper, then our magnification is 100X, and if an object on the paper is 10mm long (easily measured with a millimeter ruler) then its actual size is of course one tenth of a millimeter.

Drawings can be easily made also. One simply follows the outline of the image with a sharp pencil.

When using this method it is helpful to take off the top lens of the microscope condenser in order to get a more even light on the paper if objectives of 16mm focus or more are used (25, 32, etc.). The complete condenser is used for the shorter focus objectives (8, 4, etc.). The room should be fairly dark and if possible the paper shaded against reflected rays from the bright mounts of the objectives, etc.

If the same specimen is to be projected for some

---

* This is due to the fact that the eye sees through the microscope a virtual image of the object, while the image on the paper or on the plate of a photomicrographic camera is a real image. The virtual image is seen by the eye as if it were located in space ten inches away from the eye. The rates of comparative magnifications seen by the eye in the microscope are based on this principle, that is, the magnification of the microscope is the ratio of the apparent size of the object as seen through the microscope to the size of the object as it appears to the unaided eye at a distance of ten inches.

time and our light source is very powerful and hot it is necessary to put a water cell between the lamp and the condenser to cool the light. A piece of good heat absorbing glass can also be used if it is more practical to do so. Measurements made directly with the microscope are discussed in Chapter IX under measuring accessories.

How to Center a Microscope Condenser if Equipped with a Centering Mount

Under *condensers* in Chapter II it was mentioned that highly corrected condensers need very careful manipulation and focusing. Obviously their centering is also of *paramount importance*. This is the reason for the centering mounts which are actuated by centering screws.

The centering procedure is really quite simple. The 16mm objective with a 6 or 10X ocular is used. The microscope and lamp are set up for illumination A (see Chapter III). The condenser iris is closed down as far as it will go and the objective is focused *up* higher than its usual position when an objective is in focus. A point is reached where the eye sees the outline of the condenser iris very clearly in the field of the microscope. If the iris is in the center of the field it is centered, if it is not, it can be put in the center of the field by using the centering screws of the condenser. For a final check up and adjustment the iris is opened so its margin nearly coincides with the margin of the field of the 16mm objective and the final adjustment made with the centering screws. If the microscope lamp is equipped with an iris be sure to open the lamp iris all the way in order not to confuse its image with that of the condenser iris.

This method will work only with those centering mounts which move the iris and the condenser simultaneously. It will not work if the iris is decenterable and independent of the centering movement of the condenser. In such cases the field is carefully observed and the condenser centered to the point where it delivers the most brilliant light. One must be sure while doing this that the condenser iris *is not* decentered. It is best to center the condenser when the 16mm objective is in focus on a very transparent object such as a diatome or a blood smear. In any case, a highly corrected condenser *must* be properly centered for good results.

Visualization and Special Methods

An object is seen when the light from it reaches the retina of the eye and the resulting photochemical action initiates nerve impulses which are interpreted by the brain. The *human* eye can see only with radiations from .40 to .70 microns and is most sensitive to yellow green light of about .55 microns. Shorter radiations (ultra violet) or longer radiations (infra red) cannot be seen by the eyes and photographic recording is necessary. The amounts of vision and color sensitivity of different people varies from normal, to deficient, to complete color blindness. It is important that the microscopist know what limitations, if any, his vision has and he should understand enough color theory to be able to use color filters effectively in microscopy.

If there are two transparent regions of different refractive index in the object examined under the microscope the light passing through the region of contact will be bent and the shape of the material is interpreted from the bent light or refraction image. By this means the refractive index may be determined. The material is immersed successively in fluids of different known index until the boundary between them disappears. When the material is of different index there is usually a bright line surrounding the specimen. If this bright line, the "Becke line" moves in toward the specimen as the microscope is raised the specimen is of higher refractive index than the surrounding fluid.

When the specimen contains planes which reflect light it may be seen in part by the reflection images. Transparent materials like tissue cultures are seen as a combination of these two types of images and with the Köhler method of illumination very little detail may be visible. Contrast and as a result some detail may appear as the diaphragm of the microscope condenser is closed. The resolving power is reduced accordingly but there is no choice except to use other methods, e.g. staining.

When the different parts of the image have different colors then the specimen is seen from its color images. This is the usual method of making material visible and many dyes are used in microscopy. Color filters between the lamp and the microscope may be used to increase the contrast and detail seen in colored specimens. A filter of complementary color increases contrast and a filter of about the same color as the object reveals detail.

Portions of coherent waves of light interfere with each other, making brighter and darker regions called diffraction patterns and the image seen is a result of these patterns.

Materials which are affected by polarized light, as

described in Chapter VIII also give specific color images which are helpful in visualization.

The image of the object examined with the microscope formed on the retina of the eye is usually a combination of the several different kinds of images rather than a single one. A working knowledge of the kinds of images assists in the comprehension of what is seen and lessens the likelihood of misinterpretation. Great care is necessary when the object viewed is close to the border line of smallness which may actually be seen with the microscope.*

The Care of the Microscope

Good microscopy requires ability, practice and the *proper care of the equipment used*. The microscope is a precision instrument, manufactured with valuable materials by highly skilled labor. If properly taken care of it will last for many years but *one* bad careless moment may ruin it.

If a microscope is going to be moved from one place to another, this must be done carefully and holding it by the *arm*. Better yet with one hand holding the arm and the other beneath the base of the instrument. When not in use it should be placed in its case or covered in some way to protect it from dust. If it has been stored in a very cold room and it is brought into a warm laboratory for use, let it warm up to room temperature before using it.

One would not think of reading for an hour with dirty and finger printed spectacles, yet many people try to use microscopes with dirty lenses. All its optical parts, from the mirror right up to the eye lens of

* .0002 mm or .2 of a micron.

the ocular, must be scrupulously clean and free from dust and finger prints. The latter are usually responsible for "fogginess" when observing an object. Dust should be brushed off first with a camel's hair brush and then the lens surface gently wiped with lens paper or a very soft clean cloth. Optical glass is softer than the ordinary glass and it is easily scratched, therefore, don't use a rough cloth on it. For the same reason dust particles should be brushed off first for if they are harder than the glass they will scratch it as they are wiped off.

If there is dust inside or on the eyepieces it is seen as small particles in the field. This can be checked by rotating the eyepiece. If the particles rotate also, we know that they are not part of the object but rather dust particles in the ocular which then must be cleaned. Watch out for finger prints on the front lenses of the objectives and the lower and upper surfaces of the ocular lenses, also on the condensers.

If a liquid preparation without a cover glass is touched by the front lens of the objective we must wipe it off first before using the objective again. It is a good idea to always leave an ocular in the tube of the microscope to prevent dust from falling on to the back lens of the objective, or if we have a binocular, on the prisms of the binocular body. If however dust does fall in, it is necessary to blow it out with an ear syringe after loosening it first with a camel's hair brush. If we try to blow it out with the mouth, minute saliva particles or moisture from our breath adhere to the lens or prism surfaces and are difficult to remove. When compressed air (which is often available in laboratories) is used, the nozzle which delivers it, should be covered with an absorbent filter to catch any tiny oil droplets from the compressor.

Fine scratches on the front lens of the objective or the top lens of the ocular can be seen with a 6X hand magnifier. If the condition is bad these lenses must be sent to the factory for repair.

Objectives are composed of several lens elements, they are carefully centered and mounted in relation to each other. Never take an objective apart, *this should be done only by an expert.* The only exception are those objectives which are divisible to give two different magnifications and can be used either with or without their front mount in position. In such cases again watch for finger prints on the lower surface of the upper lens assembly.

The dry objectives may be cleaned with a little distilled water when necessary or in some cases with lens paper dampened with *very little* xylene, then wiped dry immediately. The front lens of an oil immersion objective and the top lens of a condenser should be cleaned with xylene in the same manner after oil has been used with them. Never soak them with xylene, a little is all that is necessary and then wipe them dry. *Never leave oil on an oil immersion lens or a condenser overnight.* Cedar oil is gummy and when it drys it is difficult to remove. Always wipe it off when you are through for the day and don't use more oil than necessary when working with it.

The microscope stand itself is usually finished with reagent proof enamels or metal plating. The only care it needs, other than lubrication in the proper places, is to keep it clean and free from dust. It can be wiped off from time to time with a soft cloth. If immersion oil falls upon the stage or other part of the microscope it can be wiped off with xylene or alcohol.

The bearing surfaces of the coarse adjustment should

be wiped off from time to time with xylene or with a thin oil, then a fine film of vaseline can be used on them to keep them properly lubricated. The fine adjustment usually needs no lubrication for many years. This is tricky and should be done only at the factory or by an expert microscope repair man.

Sometimes the coarse adjustment gets loose, that is the tube moves down by its own weight. This is dangerous and should be corrected immediately. This can be done very easily. The various manufacturers have different methods of taking care of this and when the microscope is purchased inquiry should always be made regarding this point. At this writing, this condition can be corrected on the Bausch & Lomb, Spencer and Leitz microscopes by tightening the screws which hold the plate over the pinion of the coarse adjustment. This can be done with a screw driver of the proper size. It is thus possible to get exactly the right friction and resistance on the coarse adjustment pinion. Zeiss has an arrangement which works as follows: holding both coarse adjustment buttons firmly, one with each hand, the left hand button is loosened by turning it counter clockwise and the right hand button tightened by turning it clockwise. In this manner the proper resistance can be arrived at. By left and right we mean having the microscope in the working position with the arm toward the worker and the tube away from the worker; *we do not mean the opposite.* If the rack and the pinion, or either are damaged, then they must be replaced.

When the prisms of a binocular microscope have been displaced in some manner by a knock, shipping, etc. do not attempt to fix them yourself. Always send the microscope to the factory to have this done. This is a very difficult job and there are very few independent repair men who can do it. In New York we know of only one such person qualified to do this job properly.

The same is true of the stereoscopic binocular microscopes (see Chapter VI) but with these instruments, very often the trouble is not in the prisms, but rather that the objectives are not properly in line with the prisms of the binocular body. This adjustment is not so difficult and many repair men can take care of it properly. It is better not to attempt this however unless one is qualified and trained to do it.

Testing Objective Lenses

Testing microscope objectives is a very difficult task. Only very experienced microscopists who know how to control *all* the factors affecting the images formed by two good objectives, can pass on which one of the two is the better lens. The quality of modern objectives, manufactured by all the reputable firms, is now so high, that with very few exceptions one can be sure that all new modern objectives turned out by these firms are excellent. If the exception turns up the manufacturer will probably be very glad to exchange it for one which is up to standard.

Never make a rash snap decision on the quality of a certain lens. The comparison test must have been made very carefully with all the factors perfectly controlled. An experienced microscopist can make a poor lens appear better than a good one might appear in the hands of a poor microscopist by the manipulation of the light, condenser, etc. The proper judgment of lenses cannot be taught in a book, it comes only with long and varied experience. Instructions for the use of *test plates* and *test objects* are given by Beck (1938), Belling (1930) and Spitta (1920). Allen (1940) also explores this subject in his book.

In deciding whether or not a used objective should be purchased one should examine it thoroughly with a 6X magnifier looking for scratches and pits on its front lens. If there are many *light* scratches or one or two deep ones or if it has one or two pits around the center, then one should not buy it unless one is willing to pay to have it repaired. *Tiny* pits around the edge are not serious and a lens should not be condemned because of them. Try it on a microscope with illumination "A" (Chapter III) and see if it gives a good sharp image. Flatness of field is secondary. Resolution and sharpness of detail are much more important. A good blood smear is an adequate test object for the following test which can be made by the average person. Using the same microscope, the same light, the same part of the object *and every other factor as equal as possible* try a new objective of about the same characteristics. If the used lens suffers very much by comparison it probably should not be purchased unless it is only dirty. Check that point. Sometimes fogginess of the image is caused by the crystallization of the cement between the elements of the objective. This is serious for this condition cannot be corrected in some *old* objectives. It is cheaper to buy, in such a case, a new one or a factory rebuilt lens. The crystallization can be seen by holding the lens up to the light and looking through it with a long focus hang magnifier of as high a magnification as practical. If this is done *just right* the crystallization can be seen in the form of little stars in the lens.

In closing let us repeat that the testing of lenses is difficult and it is always better to get the opinion of an experienced *microscopist* who has tested lenses for many years. As a practical suggestion regarding this we might mention that usually a branch office of a microscope *manufacturer* will try to help if they have available in their staff a technical man. Unfortunately there are very few microscope *dealers* who employ persons who have been sufficiently trained to make such tests. If an unbiased experienced microscopist is not available it is better to go to the manufacturer or to a *thoroughly reliable experienced* dealer of microscopes.

Chapter VI

THE STEREOSCOPIC MICROSCOPE

As ITS name implies, this type of microscope has been designed to show us the third dimension of an object. It enables us to see the depth of a specimen as well as its other two dimensions, the length and the width. Monobjective microscopes cannot show us the depth of an object except in a very limited way. Stereoscopic microscopes are never called "monobjective" because they use "paired objectives." That is, two matched objectives are mounted together converging toward each other in the same mount. The monobjective microscopes operate with only *one* objective at one time, although there may be two, three, or four objectives on the nosepiece.

Objects of all kinds, exactly as they appear in nature and without any preparation may be placed under the lenses of a stereoscopic microscope and studied with magnifications of from 5 to 150 diameters. The resulting image appears to the eye *right side up,* that is, it is not inverted as is the case when the monobjective compound microscope is used.

Obviously, it is very much easier to use dissecting instruments in the natural way than to have to remember to work backwards which is necessary when the image viewed is inverted. Therefore, the stereoscopic microscopes are used a great deal for dissections which require a high magnification. Because of this they are also often called "dissecting binoculars." Another name for them is "Greenough microscopes."

These instruments are used a great deal in high schools, colleges and Universities for observations and work in biology, geology, chemistry and metallurgy. In fact, they are useful whenever it is necessary to examine objects with magnifications greater than those given by the hand magnifiers, but not greater than 100 or 150 diameters.* Entomologists use them constantly either as they are or with the addition of special apparatus to hold and turn the insects to the desired position. They are also very helpful to examine the general condition of sections made with a microtome before the final mounting and staining operations are performed.

In industry they are used for the examination of many materials and objects which will be part of the final product. Sizes and tolerances are checked with these microscopes. Also defects of various kinds such as scratches, irregularities, pits, etc. Many manufacturers have found it extremely advantageous to check such defects *before* the parts are incorporated into the final product and thus avoid complaints and difficulties later.

* An interesting recent development which appears to have considerable merit in the study of permanently mounted specimens with the stereoscopic microscope is the use of methacrylate plastics as mounting media for biological specimens.

Puckett, W. O., 1940—Ethyl methacrylate as a mounting medium for embryological specimens—Science, Vol. 91, pp. 625-626.

Puckett, W. O., 1941—The methacrylate plastics as mounting media for biological materials. Anatomical Record—Vol. 80, No. 4, Aug. 25.

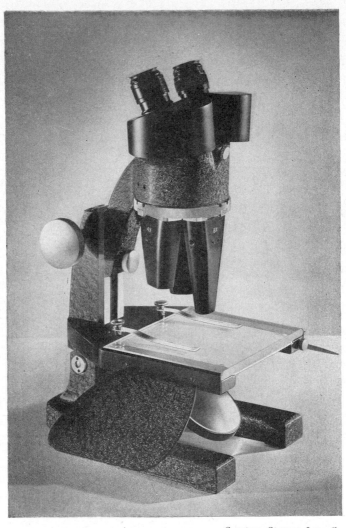

FIGURE 73

A stereoscopic microscope with inclined binocular body, horse shoe base, mirror, hand rests and revolving nosepiece for three paired objectives.

Stereoscopic microscopes are also becoming increasingly popular among amateur microscopists and hobbyists of all kinds. The reason for this is that generally no special preparation of the object is necessary before observing it. One can take a little gold, put it under the microscope and thus explore gorgeous and breathtaking mountains and caverns of this precious metal. A fly or a spider temporarily anaesthetized can be studied to our heart's content. The eye of a fly appears like a beautiful gem, cut and polished by the finest artisan of Amsterdam. Natural crystals and even rocks and colored stones are breathtaking in their beauty when viewed with one of these fascinating instruments. The wing of a butterfly astounds us with the brilliance and beauty of its colors and the geometrical perfection of its details. In short, to use one of these instruments for the first time is to open the first door leading to the "world of the little."

It is true that stereoscopic microscopes cannot reveal to us the very fine details of a specimen which require much greater magnifications. However, perhaps one should look at the forest first before examining and classifying its trees.

Construction and Parts

Why does a stereoscopic microscope show us the third dimension of an object? Because the object is observed from two different sides at the same time. When we use both our eyes to look at an orange, we are looking at it from two sides and our brain blends the two images into one which gives us a good idea of its roundness, color, etc. When the stereoscopic microscope is used the result is the same for we are simply aiding our eyes to see smaller objects and details than is possible otherwise. The convergence of the objectives and of the ocular tubes is so arranged in the microscope that it is about the same as the natural convergence of our eyes when reading, writing, etc.

Now let us study the construction of the instrument step by step. By referring to fig. 73 we see that in general it looks somewhat like a conventional microscope, but we notice several differences. We have the usual horse shoe base and mirror, but there is no condenser because the low magnifications of the objectives, and their low N.A.'s do not require the use of a condenser. We observe two wings on either side of the stage. These are "hand rests" to support our wrists and hands in order to give us better stability when performing a difficult dissection. The stage is of glass instead of being opaque, and it is easily removable from the microscope so that we can clean it after a dissection. We can make it opaque however if we want to, by inserting under it an opaque plate. This plate is usually white on one side and black on the other so that we may obtain the best contrast for the coloring of the specimen. Then, we find the objectives which may be only one "pair" or two or three pairs. If more than one pair, they are usually mounted in a revolving nosepiece or some other type of "quick changer." Now we come to the prism binocular body with its ocular tubes with provision for variations of interpupillary distances. This binocular body may have either vertical tubes or inclined tubes like those shown in the microscope fig. 73. Finally, we see that there is only one focusing adjustment. There is no fine adjustment. The focusing adjustment is a rack and pinion actuated by the usual adjustment buttons. The fine adjustment is not necessary because, since the magnifications used are not very large, the rack and pinion is adequate to give us a precise focus.

In modern stereoscopic microscopes it is possible to remove the horseshoe base and mirror assembly from the rest of the instrument so that the stage of the microscope will rest on the table. This is convenient when reflected rather than transmitted light is to be used, that is, when the specimen is going to be illuminated only from above.

Stereoscopic microscopes are also mounted on stands which have large and heavy vertical and horizontal arms so that larger surfaces may be covered more easily or to view specimens in aquaria, etc. There are also other types of specialized stands. All these types however, are only a means of adapting the optical system of the microscope to specific purposes so that certain specimens can be observed in a more convenient manner than would be possible with the conventional stereoscopic microscope stand.

Let us now examine the optical system by referring to fig. 74. We see immediately that a stereoscopic microscope is really two different compound microscopes mounted together. Each one of these two microscopes has an objective and an eyepiece, but between these two lenses, there is a prism assembly. Their chief purpose is to "erect" the image seen by the eye so that it will appear right side up instead of reversed as is the case in the regular compound microscopes. These prisms also may be designed to change slightly the direction of the light. One of the American manufacturers does this so that the convergence of the oculars is less than that of the objectives. They claim that by using this construction it is possible to obtain greater stereoscopy combined with maximum comfort. The chief purpose of the prisms however is to erect the image.

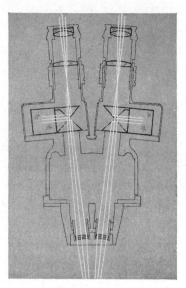

Courtesy Spencer Lens Co.

FIGURE 74

Light path in stereoscopic microscope.

In stereoscopic microscopes the objectives are designed to give only comparatively low magnifications, usually between 1X and 8X. There are also paired negative objectives which form an image smaller than the object and it is then magnified by the oculars to the desired amount. Such objectives are marked .6X, .7X, etc. This means that such objectives will form an image six tenths or seven tenths as large as the object actually is. This seems strange unless we keep in mind the fact that the lower the magnification the larger the field of view and vice versa. Therefore, when the size of field is more important than a higher possible magnification, the size of the field of view is enlarged by reducing the initial image. It is then magnified by the oculars. Thus we see that in stereoscopic microscopes the emphasis on magnification is laid on the oculars, not on the objectives. In the monobjective microscopes it is exactly the opposite.

The proper alignment of the prisms and objectives is extremely important in these instruments because otherwise the eyes of the worker cannot blend the two images into one and terrific eye strain develops. Also the prisms may be all right but the objectives may not be in proper alignment with them, if such is the case, the same kind of eye strain results. The alignment operation of the prisms is very difficult and should be performed only at the factory or by a person trained for this at the factory. The alignment of the objectives is easier but also requires experience before it can be done successfully. If when one looks through one of these microscopes one feels an uncomfortable drawing of the eyes, or if when focusing on a small spot on the object one sees two images of that spot, then either the prisms, the objectives, or both are out of alignment. It is possible to decide what is the trouble in the following manner: Place in the proper place in one of the oculars a cross hair disc. Put the ocular in one of the tubes of the microscope and using one eye only with this ocular (the objective is in place also) focus on a small spot of the object carefully. Place the spot in the center of the cross hairs. Rotate the prism body slowly to the limit of its possible excursion and then back again while watching the position of the spot on the cross hairs. If the spot does not stay near center of the cross hairs, then that prism assembly may be out of line. Do the same using the ocular on the other ocular tube and determine whether or not that other prism assembly is also out. *If either or both* are out, then the microscope should go to the factory immediately. If the prisms are O.K. but we still get eye strain or a double image, then the trouble is with the alignment of the objectives. As we said before this is an easier adjustment, it is performed also with the aid of the cross hair disc using one tube first and then the other. The tiny centering

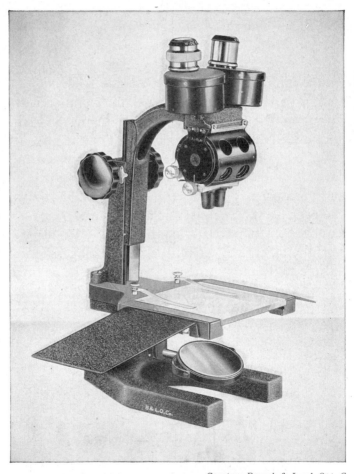

Courtesy Bausch & Lomb Opt. Co.

FIGURE 75

Stereoscopic microscope with vertical binocular body and drum nosepiece for three paired objectives.

screws of the objectives are worked against each other with a small screw driver until the spot appears near center of the cross hairs on both sides. Although easier, this adjustment requires considerable practice before it can be done well and rapidly.

The important point is that if there is any eye strain, or if a double image is present this condition should be corrected at once for it may be harmful to the worker.

Another very important point to remember is that up until the present writing, the objectives of a stereo-

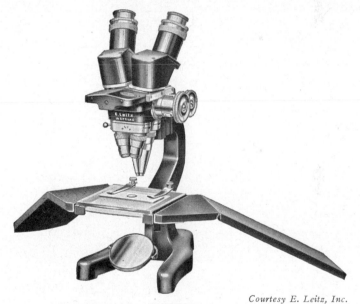

Courtesy E. Leitz, Inc.

FIGURE 76

Stereoscopic microscope with sliding type rapid objective changer.

scopic microscope can be used *only* on the particular microscope to which they have been aligned. Also, in microscopes equipped with a quick changing device (nosepiece, drum, etc.) they will work properly *only* if used in the particular position of the changer where they were lined up. *We cannot take the objectives from one stereoscopic microscope and use them on another, or change their position around in the nosepiece.* For this reason, it is a good idea to put the same number or mark on the objectives and on the microscope stand to which they belong. This is especially important in places where there are in use several stereoscopic microscopes. Many repair bills and difficulties would be saved by educational institutions if they took the trouble to mark their stereoscopic microscopes, both the stands and the objectives, in the manner suggested above.

The limit of Numerical Aperture possible with paired objectives for use with stereoscopic microscope seems to be around 0.12. At least, until the present time we have not heard of paired objectives of this type having higher numerical apertures. If we must have materially higher values of N.A. we must go to the regular monobjective microscopes.

The oculars are paired, and in modern stereoscopic microscopes they are usually of the wide field type designed to give as large a field of view as possible. With the lower magnifications it is possible to get as large a field of view as one inch or slightly more. Usually some provision is made in the oculars so that they will receive a cross hair disc or a measuring disc. They are usually marked with their magnification, i.e., 9X ,12X, 15X, etc. This value when multiplied by the magnification of the objectives gives us the total magnification of the combination used.

The photomicrographs of a wine fly shown in fig. 78 with their magnifications, may be helpful in deciding the magnification needed for a particular problem. Note how the size of the field decreases as the mag-

FIGURE 77

A small stereoscopic microscope.

nification increases and vice versa. Also note the increase in details with the higher magnifications. The various manufacturers usually show in their catalogs of stereoscopic microscopes a table which gives the size of the field obtained with their combinations of objectives and oculars.

How to Use the Stereoscopic Microscope

Before attempting to work with this instrument we must make sure that the prisms and the objectives are properly aligned. This test was described previously. Once this has been determined, and if we are sure also that our optical system is clean, we proceed as follows:

a—For transparent objects which we wish to examine with transmitted light:

The object is placed upon the stage of the microscope. The opaque plate is removed from its place under the stage. The light is directed upward by means of the microscope mirror. We can use either the plane or the concave surface of the mirror, whichever gives us the better light. If a microscope lamp is being used let us make sure that a ground glass is in place in the

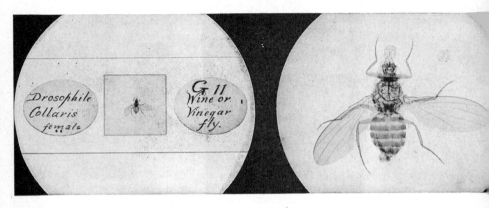

1X   6.3X

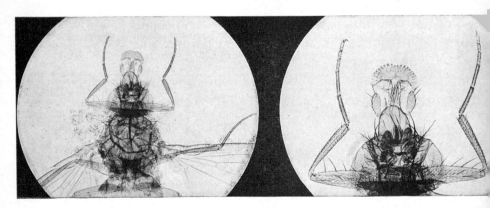

12X   24X

Courtesy Spencer L.

FIGURE 78

Photomicrographs of the Wine Fly showing decrease of field as magnification increases and more details are revealed.

lamp because neither Köhler nor Critical illumination are practical with a stereoscopic microscope. Some specimens show best when the mirror is in its central position and the light thrown directly upward into the microscope. Others require setting the mirror to one side so that the specimen is lighted obliquely. By light-

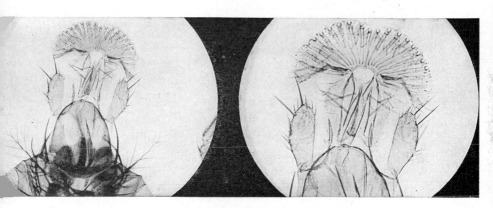

45X   72X

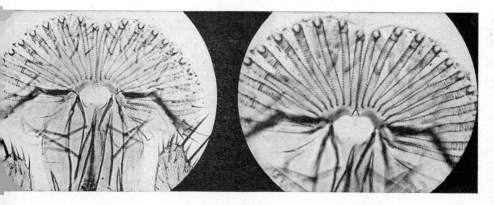

108X   144X

Courtesy Spencer Lens Co.

FIGURE 78 (*Continued*)

Photomicrographs of the Wine Fly showing decrease of field as magnification increases and more details are revealed.

ing them in this manner, sometimes more details are revealed.

The interpupillary distance of the prism bodies is adjusted to the right position for the eyes of the worker, and the microscope is focused upon the object by means of the rack and pinion buttons. If necessary the intensity of the light is controlled by means of the iris diaphragm of the lamp or by neutral tint filters. If both eyes are not in perfect focus, one is focused first with the rack and pinion and then, leaving that adjustment alone, the other eye is focused with the extendable ocular tube or by the means provided by the manufacturer to do so. Some stereoscopic microscopes do not have one of their ocular tubes extendable, but the adjustment can be made nevertheless by raising or lowering slightly one of the oculars if it fits in the ocular tube in a friction mount. This accomplishes the same thing. Some of the older microscopes have their higher power objectives mounted so that one of the pair can be focused up and down. In that case the individual eye focus is adjusted by using the rack and pinion for one eye and the focusing adjustment of the objective for the other. In this way the proper balance can be reached for both eyes.

b—For opaque objects which require incident light from above.

The specimen is placed upon the stage and a beam of light is directed from above *so that it falls on the object at the desired angle.* This angle is very important and varies according to the specimen. This point was discussed in greater detail in Chapter III under illumination of opaque objects. If the magnification used is fairly high, from 30X up, it is generally necessary to remove the ground glass from the lamp using only a clear blue or green filter instead. In this way we can place a powerful spot of light on the object. If there is danger that the heat from the lamp will damage the specimen, we can reduce the heat by placing a water cell between the lamp and the object, or else, a piece of "heat absorbing glass" can be used in the lamp. These glasses are sold by the microscope manufacturers and

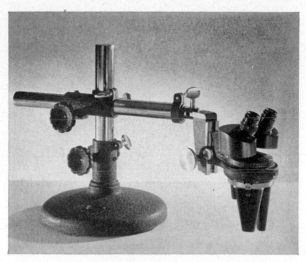

Courtesy Spencer Lens Co.

FIGURE 79

Large table stand with stereoscopic microscope.

they are very useful and practical for this purpose. Also, the specially designed low voltage lamps for stereoscopic microscopes give a fairly cool light. Fig. 80 illustrates such a lamp. There is also the Nicholas Illuminator, sold by Bausch and Lomb, which is similar and also gives a small intense spot of fairly cool light.

We should always use the background which gives us the best contrast. Some objects require the white surface of the contrast plate while with others the black

FIGURE 80

Small lamp for stereoscopic microscopes.

side should be used. One must try them both if in doubt and see which is better. The focusing is done as described before under examination with transmitted light.

Some workers like to attach the lamp to the microscope itself whenever it is possible to do so. The special microscope lamps can be usually attached in some manner to the binocular body of the instrument. This has the advantage of eliminating the lamp from the table and thus have more room near at hand for dissecting instruments, petri dishes, specimens, etc.

With seeds and other small objects lighted from above, there is often enough room between them to allow the use of a combination of incident and transmitted light. At times this method of lighting is useful and should be tried when possible.

How to Take Care of the Stereoscopic Microscope

Generally the same rules given for the care of the monobjective microscopes are applicable to the stereoscopic instruments. However, since these are used somewhat differently, the following points should be kept in mind.

Always wash the stage glass plate with soap and water after a dissection. The same is true of the background plate. Dry them thoroughly before putting them back on the microscope.

If sea water, etc., falls upon the stage of the microscope, don't leave it wet overnight. Wash it and dry it. Otherwise, the water may rust the metal mountings which hold the stage in position.

Always be sure that the prisms and the objectives are in perfect alignment and scrupulously clean. The prisms should be checked from time to time to see if any foreign matter has accumulated on their surfaces, usually on their upper surfaces. If so they should be cleaned as soon as possible with a soft cloth or lens paper and the lint blown out with an ear syringe. Those little wooden rods which have soft cotton wrapped around both ends called "cutips" are very useful for this purpose. All drug stores sell them. In humid locations such as marine biological laboratories one must keep everlastingly at this in order to have the microscope always in first class working condition. If the condition is very bad, it is necessary to send the microscope to the factory for cleaning of its optical parts or to have a properly qualified person do so.

Chapter VII

THE METALLURGICAL MICROSCOPE

THE science of metallurgy is dependent to a great degree on the study of the structure of the metals. This requires the use of a microscope. It is no longer enough to know the weight of a metal and its reaction to a chemical attack in order to decide whether or not it is adequate for a certain function. Now it is not only necessary to know what kind of metal it is, we must also examine its component characteristics and measure the size of its minute crystal grains and perhaps even the distance between them. It is also necessary to compare specimens which according to the usual tests are nearly identical but which when examined with a microscope prove to be quite different in their structure. Nowadays a metallurgical laboratory is not complete without a good metallurgical microscope and a photomicrographic camera to record the observations made.

Generally, the microscope is used by metal industries to examine the form of the sand in the foundry; to determine the crystalline structure of metals as they pass through the different processes of manufacture; and to check the finished product in regard to its surface qualities, its contours and correct size.

Metallurgical microscopy differs so much, in so many ways from conventional microscopy that it has been necessary to design special microscopes for this work.

FIGURE 81

Metallurgical microscope with independent light unit attached to tube of the microscope.

These microscopes are called "metallurgical microscopes." These instruments are necessary because metal specimens being opaque cannot be examined with transmitted light. Such specimens must be examined with light coming from above, not from below therefore the substage condenser is useless and is eliminated from a metallurgical microscope. In these instruments the microscope objective in combination with a vertical illuminator acts as a condenser in addition to performing its regular function of forming and magnifying the image. Naturally, since we do not need a substage condenser its focusing adjustments are also eliminated.

Some metallurgical microscopes do have a condenser and mirror, but these parts are there only when it is necessary to use the same microscope both for metallurgical and transmitted light work.

Since metallurgical specimens are usually much thicker than a microscope slide, and since this thickness varies considerably according to the specimens, it is desirable to have a great deal more room available when necessary between the objective and the top surface of the stage. This is brought about by either or both of two possibilities:

1. The tube is mounted on a slideway which operates independently of the regular focusing adjustments.

2. The stage is constructed so that it is movable up and down by a rack and pinion. This has the advantage of giving us the possibility of making the coarse focus by moving the stage, that is, we can focus the object to the objective lens instead of the lens to the object. There are times, as we shall see later, when this possibility is very useful. Generally metallurgical microscopes have both of these possible adjustments, but at least one is necessary.

The objectives used for metallurgy are also different from standard objectives. They may be also achromatic, fluorite and apochromatic, but they look different and are different than the objectives on the ordinary compound microscope. Since they are generally used with a vertical illuminator mounted above them, and since it has been determined that an objective works better with such illuminators when its back lens is close to the reflector of the illuminator, metallurgical objectives are constructed in short mounts. The usual upper metal mount of a high power objective is eliminated so that the back lens element can be brought closer to the vertical illuminator. The low power objectives, i.e., 48mm, 32mm, are not especially mounted because they are "short mounts" anyway, but the high power lenses are especially mounted.

They also differ from standard objectives in that they have been calculated for use *without* a cover glass. This is obviously necessary since a cover glass is not used on metallurgical specimens. It is well to remember therefore, that a high power metallurgical objective should

Courtesy E. Leitz, Inc.

Figure 82

Vertical illuminator—Has both a prism and a plate glass reflector.

not be used on a standard microscope to view a specimen covered with a cover glass. Also a regular high power objective does not work satisfactorily on a metallurgical microscope when examining a specimen which *does not* have a cover glass over it. Here again, as far as the low power objectives are concerned, it does not make any difference for they are not materially affected by cover glass thickness.

Another point which we must bear in mind is that some manufacturers calculate their metallurgical objec-

Courtesy Bausch & Lomb Opt. Co.

FIGURE 83

A binocular metallurgical microscope with electric vertical illuminator.

tives for use with longer tube lengths than regular objectives. It is well to always inquire about this when purchasing a metallurgical objective.

Finally, as regards the general construction of a metallurgical microscope, it also differs from the conventional in that it seldom has a revolving nosepiece. The vertical illuminator * takes the place of the nosepiece.

---

* For various types see Chapter III under Illumination of Opaque Objects.

Usually the vertical illuminators in metallurgical microscopes are equipped with a quick change receptacle so that the objectives can be changed more quickly than by screwing them into place. Classroom metallurgical microscopes are sometimes equipped with a revolving nosepiece attached to the vertical illuminator, but the standard metallurgical microscopes seldom have a nosepiece because this increases materially the distance between the back lens of the objective and the vertical illuminator. As we said before it is better to keep this

Courtesy Spencer Lens Co.

FIGURE 84

Biological microscope equipped for metallurgical work.

distance as short as possible. For routine work however the revolving nosepiece is useful and practical.

The rest of the metallurgical microscope, (i.e., the oculars, the focusing adjustments, and the inclination joint) is very similar to the conventional microscope.

Metallurgical microscopes, like the conventional instruments, may be monoculars or binoculars. Naturally, if it is a binocular, provision is made to substitute the binocular body with a single tube so that photomicrographs can be taken with the same microscope.

As we have seen above, in order to work quickly and effectively when examining metals the specialized metallurgical microscope is necessary. If it is not possible to obtain one, a conventional microscope may be used by adding the necessary accessories but such a converted instrument would have many limitations. However, it can be used for the examination of many specimens for as we have said before all specialized microscopes are fundamentally similar to the conventional instrument.

The Use of the Metallurgical Microscope for Both Metallurgical Work and Conventional Work. Also the Use of a Conventional Microscope for Metallurgical Work.

The following questions are often asked (a) Most of my work is metallurgical, but occasionally I must use transmitted light for some specimens, can I use the same microscope for both purposes? also, (b) Most of my work is with transmitted light, but can I adapt a regular microscope for metallurgical work? Although we have answered both of the above questions in a general way we shall be more specific now. The answers are:

(a)—Yes, by equipping the metallurgical microscope with a condenser (they usually have a removable disc in the center of their opaque stages) and by substituting the vertical illuminator with a revolving nosepiece or a single nosepiece adapter. Likewise, if the specimens examined are going to be covered with a cover glass the regular long mount objectives must be purchased also. This means two sets of objectives for the higher powers, beginning *at least* with the 8mm, preferably with the 16mm one set for metallurgical work (short mounts), and one set for transmitted light work (long mounts for use with cover glasses).

(b)—Yes, by purchasing a vertical illuminator (see illumination of opaque objects, Chapter III) and by adding also the necessary short mount objectives for use without a cover glass.

Our recommendation is that whenever possible two types of microscopes be purchased, for by the time the necessary accessories are purchased for either, to adapt it for the other work, the difference in price is not excessive. The convenience and time saved is well worth this difference. If the same instrument *must* be used for both types of work, then the basic instrument purchased should be the one designed for most of the contemplated work and accessories purchased to adapt it to do the other work.

Preparation of Metallurgical Specimens

This subject can be treated here only in a very general way for metals differ greatly from each other. There are hard and soft metals, ferrous and nonferrous, as well as alloys of many different characteristics. The

treatment or preparation of each classification is different in its details and the various methods have been
evolved through the years to their different applications. For exact information therefore the specialized
textbooks must be consulted.

Since the purpose of the microscopic study of a metal
specimen is to observe its physical structure, constituents, foreign particles, grain size, etc. it is necessary to
secure the best possible plane across it. If this plane is
attained, it is possible to see clearly and to study the
various characteristics and constituents of the specimen.

By grinding and polishing the specimen we can get
the plane surface but before it can be studied it is necessary to etch it with the proper chemical to bring out
the structure which we wish to study. The different
constituents of the metal react in a different way to the
chemical attack to which they are subjected.

Unless we have available the necessary grinding ma-
chinery, specially developed and sold for this purpose,
the grinding operations are slow and require considerable patience. They must be performed however in
order to prepare a mirror surface which will take properly the final etching.

Some metals which are not too hard can be prepared
to a great extent by the use of a microtome. Obviously
the only metals which can be prepared in this way are
those softer than the steel of the microtome knife which
is going to be used. Some lead alloys and other soft
metals may be surfaced smooth enough for etching and
microscope study. Naturally this method when practical is much more rapid than the usual grinding and
polishing methods.

When small specimens are going to be prepared by

the microtome method they are sometimes embedded in one of the methacrylate resins or Bakelite. If the latter, a pure resin should be used rather than one mixed with asbestos or other fibers that will unduly wear the knife edge. A heavy rotary or sliding microtome which has a sturdy knife holder and feeding mechanism should be used. The feed is set for 1 or 2 microns. The more experience and the greater the skill of the operator the better the surface obtained.

The usual grinding and polishing operations are performed more or less in the following manner:

a—The specimen is usually a cube of about ½ inch.

b—One surface is roughly prepared with a file or a rough grinding wheel until it is as flat and plane as possible.

c—A piece of number 1 emery paper or the equivalent carborondum paper is laid over a hard flat surface such as a heavy piece of plate glass and the cube rubbed up and down *in the same direction.*

d—The emery paper is changed to one less coarse and the rubbing continued but the cube is rotated through 90 degrees so that the new scratches will go right across the first ones made.

e—This is continued through various grades of coarseness of papers until the very fine ones are reached. Each time a paper is changed the cube is rotated through 90 degrees. Many experienced workers end up with a paper of the finest grade of coarseness which has been used before.

Now we are ready for the final polishing operation necessary to bring out the required mirror surface. For this we must have a revolving disc operated by a motor.

We cover the disc with a clean soft cloth free from hard fibres. Canton flannel is often used for this purpose. A good fine polishing powder such as levigated alumina is mixed with enough water to form a milky solution, and after it is allowed to settle the top of the mixture is used. Thus we get rid of the coarser particles and our mixture is ready for the polishing disc.

When all the scratches have disappeared from the treated surface of our cube we have a beautiful mirror surface which is now ready for etching.

The proper acids or proportions of acids must be used depending on the type of the metal. For some of the pure metals even an electrolytic attack in aqua regia may be necessary. Different treatments may be necessary to bring out the individual constituents.

The treated surface can now be properly examined with the metallurgical microscope even with an oil immersion lens at very high magnifications. We must be very careful not to attempt to do so if finger prints have been left on the surface. It must be perfectly clean. It is best to examine the specimen *immediately* after etching to avoid changes due to rapid oxidation.

The Use of the Metallurgical Microscope

We shall take for our example one of the usual metallurgical microscopes such as the one illustrated in fig. 81. We shall assume that we are only interested in observing our specimen with the higher powers. For the lower powers we probably would have simply examined it with light of the proper intensity falling obliquely upon it from above. The technique would be the same for the binocular microscope except for the proper use of the binocular body (Chapter V) and the necessity of more light than would be used with a monocular.

Our microscope has a focusable stage actuated by a rack and pinion; a plate glass vertical illuminator either with a built on light source or independent as shown in the illustration; a quick change receptacle for the objectives; achromatic objectives short mount 16mm 10X, 8mm 20X, 4mm 44X, and a 1.8mm oil immersion; oculars huyghenian 5X and 10X and compensating 15X and 20X so we can reach the highest magnifications. Each objective is mounted on a ring which will fit the quick change receptacle for the objectives.

We put the 16mm objective and the ocular on the microscope. Now, if our metal cube is nice and flat on its under surface we put it on a microscope slide so we can move it around easily. If its under surface is not flat it is put in a little receptacle of some kind on top of some modeling clay or some such material so we can set it with its treated etched surface perpendicular to the axis of the objective. Naturally the etched surface is facing up toward the objective. The light from the lamp (without any ground glass) is directed toward the reflector of the vertical illuminator in a perfectly straight line, and we make sure that the reflector in turn sends it *down* toward the specimen, not up toward the ocular. This may sound silly but we have seen a student try to focus on a specimen for several minutes without success because the reflector had been rotated so that the light went up instead of down. If we move the tube of the microscope so that the front lens of the objective is about ¼ of an inch away from the specimen and our light is nearly right we can see from the side a brilliant spot of light on the specimen. Now we are ready to examine it.

If we are using a microscope lamp which is set upon the table, in other words, if our light *does not* move up and down with the tube, we can do all the preliminary focusing by moving the stage of the microscope up and down instead of the tube of the microscope. In this way we eliminate the necessity of having to line up the lamp if we move the tube a little. The slight movement of the fine adjustment will not have any serious effect on the alignment of the light.

It is helpful to have a green filter available and one or two neutral tint filters to place between our light source and the reflector of the vertical illuminator. Also other color filters are useful for certain specimens.

We now view our specimen and focus with the fine adjustment (since we have attained the primary focus with the coarse adjustment or by focusing with the stage). If there seems to be a slight fog over the image, and if we are sure that our optical system is clean, this fog is probably due to extraneous light. We close down some the iris of the vertical illuminator, or if it has no iris, we use the smaller opening which is usually provided when there is no iris. Then if we still have fog we use neutral tint filters until we have the best possible light. Sometimes it is necessary to rotate slightly the reflector of the vertical illuminator or if our light is independent of it, to move the lamp a little one way or the other. When the light is just right we can make out the structure of the metal.

It is now possible to go to the higher powers if we want to without any difficulty, always controlling the light carefully to get the best possible results with each magnification.

The oil immersion objective is used in nearly the

same way as with transmitted light. A drop of oil is carefully placed upon the specimen or upon the front lens of the objective before the objective is connected to the microscope. Oil contact is made, either by moving the tube or the stage, whichever is more convenient. As we do this we watch from the side, then the final focus is made with the fine adjustment.

We can make any measurements we wish with the aid of measuring accessories and also if we wish we can take necessary photomicrographs with a photomicrographic camera (Chapter IX).

In general the use of an electric vertical illuminator is much easier, because the intensity of light, change of filters, etc. can be more readily controlled. However, with a little practice the regular vertical illuminators give very satisfactory results. When high and low power objectives are going to be used, the combined type which permits the use of either the prism or the plate glass is very useful.

For the finest research work and for photomicrography the apochromatic short mount objectives are helpful.

The Inverted Metallurgical Microscope

Besides the standard metallurgical microscopes there are also available other types of metallurgical microscopes. We shall now study briefly the inverted metallurgical microscope.

This is a very complete instrument with many optical and mechanical parts and necessarily quite expensive. It is usually sold complete with a light source, generally an arc lamp, a side viewing or observation eyepiece and a photomicrographic camera. The heart,

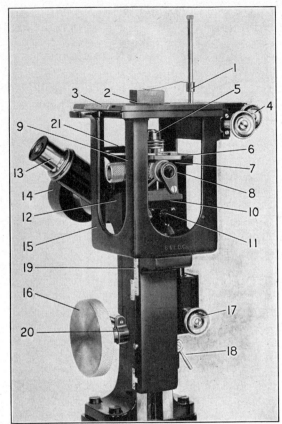

Courtesy Bausch & Lomb Opt. Co.

FIGURE 85

Inverted metallurgical microscope.

1. Specimen Holder.
2. Stage Aperture Plate.
3. Mechanical Stage Scale.
4. Mechanical Stage Adjustment Heads.
5. Objective.
6. Objective Handle.
7. Iris Diaphragm Adjusting Ring.
8. Filter Mount.
9. Vertical Illuminator Mirror Mount.
10. Stellite Mirror Housing.
11. Heat Shield Socket.
12. Microscope Body.
13. Observation Eyepiece.
14. Camera Connector.
15. Stage Casting.
16. Coarse Adjustment Head.
17. Fine Adjustment Head.
18. Reducing Gear Lever.
19. Coarse Adjustment Scale.
20. Coarse Adjustment Lock.
21. Stabilizer.

or business section of such an instrument is shown in fig. 85. The light source may come complete with its water cell, filter holder, centering device, etc. The camera is usually of the bellows type so that the distance between the microscope eyepiece and the plate can be increased or decreased. In this way the magnification on the plate can be increased or decreased within certain limits. These parts together with the "heart" part of the microscope equipment are mounted on an optical bench in order to hold all its parts rigidly in perfect alignment.

The microscope itself differs from the standard met-

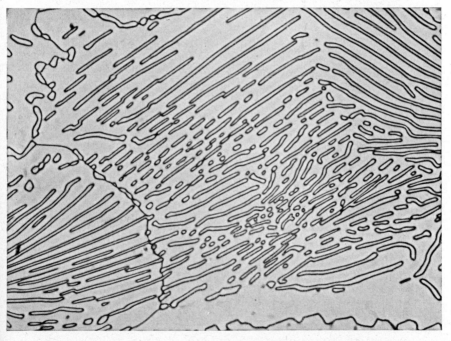

Courtesy Geo. Scherr Co.

Figure 86

Cast iron—2000X.

allurgical microscope in that it is inverted. The objectives etc. are *under* the stage instead of above it. This enables us to put on the stage a specimen of considerable size and weight. The prepared surface of the specimen is put *down* upon the stage so that the problem of adjusting it to a perpendicular position to the optical axis of the instrument is eliminated. Since the

Courtesy Geo. Scherr Co.

FIGURE 87

Stainless steel—2000X.

stage can be moved about mechanically by means of rack and pinions, we can move the specimen very gently and with complete control so that we can study any part of its prepared surface. Usually the stage is movable up and down for focusing with coarse and fine adjustments so that the optical alignment of the light will not be disturbed.

It is possible to observe the specimen, with greatly reduced light, through the observation eyepiece, then when the particular spot we want is found, it can be photographed very easily at any desired magnification within the limits of the optical system and bellow extension of the camera.

These instruments are useful and they are manufactured by microscope makers both in Europe and in the United States. Unfortunately their cost is necessarily quite high. They differ considerably in their mechanical details according to the manufacturer, but the above gives a general idea of these beautiful precision instruments. If one is purchased full instructions should be requested from the manufacturer and carefully followed.

The Bullet Comparision Microscope

This type of microscope belongs in this chapter because usually it consists of two simplified metallurgical microscopes connected with a comparison eyepiece (Chapter IX). It is a generally accepted fact that the barrel of a gun leaves certain characteristic marks on any bullet fired through it. Therefore if two bullets are compared side by side and their markings (rifling marks) are absolutely identical, then it is logical to assume or determine that these two bullets were fired from the same gun. This type of evidence is important in murder trials of course and hence, police departments all over the world as well as all ballistics laboratories, find these instruments extremely useful. Photomicrographs are always taken when a good "match" of two

Courtesy Bausch & Lomb Opt. Co.

FIGURE 88

Bullet comparison microscope with bellow extension camera.

bullets is found so that it can be used as evidence in court if necessary. The markings on a fired bullet are to the gun what finger prints are to fingers.

It is not always easy to obtain a perfect bullet match. If the bullet is badly smashed or deformed one has to do considerable searching. An expert in this work however can usually although not always find at least one small section of the bullet which can be matched to the "known" bullet if they were both fired from the same gun.

The examination or matching of bullets is made with comparatively low magnifications, somewhere between 20 and 40 diameters. However, when the "match" is made, it is sometimes blown up some when making the photomicrograph by extending the camera bellows in order to enlarge the details.

One type of bullet comparison microscope consists of two metallurgical microscopes without vertical illuminators. No vertical illuminators are necessary because at the magnifications used, it is possible to illuminate the specimens perfectly without the necessity of sending the light beam through the objective. Two powerful microscope lamps are used, one for each microscope. The test bullet and the "known" bullet are held in ingenious devices built on the microscope stages so that the bullets can be rotated and moved about. One bullet is put under the objective of each microscope. The objectives and eyepieces are matched so that they will give exactly the same magnification. Since the two microscopes are connected by the comparison eyepiece, by looking through it, half of each bullet can be seen side by side and the match made if possible. Then it is photographed.

This type of microscope can be used also for transmitted light and other types of microscope examination.
One of the two instruments can be disconnected from

Courtesy Spencer Lens Co.

FIGURE 89

Bullet comparison microscope (two metallurgical microscopes
equipped for bullet work).

the other and used as a regular microscope. In other
words, although specialized it is not entirely so. This
led to the development of the simplified more highly
specialized bullet comparison microscopes which are
less expensive and yet adequate for bullet comparison
work.

The latest simplified bullet comparison microscopes
differ from the type previously described in that they
have no microscope arms. The stages are independent

of the tubes. The tubes are attached to the comparison eyepiece and extend downward toward the stages. The only focusing adjustments are on the stages to move them up and down. The lighting unit consists of

Courtesy Spencer Lens Co.

FIGURE 90

Photomicrograph of matched bullets.

either one long light which illuminates both bullets or of two separate lamps one for each bullet. Also, there is usually an iris diaphragm over the objectives (one in each tube) to balance the light coming from each bullet to the comparison eyepiece. In this way the light reflected from a new shiny bullet can be cut down and balanced to that coming from a tarnished bullet which may reflect less light.

The camera, on both the complete and the simplified instruments, is attached to the comparison eyepiece so that the match can be photographed exactly as it is seen by the eye. Usually fairly long exposures are necessary, a matter of minutes instead of seconds.

Other Types of Metallurgical Microscopes

There are several other types of metallurgical microscopes. All are variations of the basic instrument but designed to do specific jobs more easily and rapidly.

There are the tool maker microscopes for rapid measuring and observation of tools under construction. These instruments may be more or less complicated and their possible magnifications also vary. There are also the contour projectors which in a way are metallurgical microscopes, to magnify the shadow cast by, or the surface of an opaque object. Some are used only for the shadow, others for both the shadow or the surface. The image can be seen on a semi-transparent screen. These are highly specialized instruments used for manufacturing control and for certain research problems. Their cost is necessarily high.

In closing this chapter we must state that all types of metallurgical microscopes require the same general care that is given to the conventional miscroscopes. The optical parts must be kept clean and the bearing surfaces properly lubricated. In addition the reflector of the vertical illuminator must be kept free from dust and clean. Some experience is required before the best results are possible with these instruments. The technique for their use and the preparation of materials can be mastered however with a little patience and perseverance.

Chapter VIII

THE POLARIZING MICROSCOPE

This is one of the most interesting and complete microscopes made at the present time. It is highly specialized and has many additional optical and mechanical parts when compared with the conventional microscope. The use of polarized light has made necessary the use of these additional parts. It is possible to study specimens with a standard microscope equipped with acessories which polarize the light,* but in order to do really fine work the use of the specialized polarizing microscope is necessary.

The first polarizing microscopes were produced in France between 1833 and 1855 by Nachet. They were considered only as novelties to demonstrate the phenomena of polarized light and the strange action apparent in some crystals when they were illuminated in this manner. Early workers who tried to make practical application of what they saw became confused by the complexity of their observations, and for many years little progress was made. Practical use of these instruments really began about 1877 with the development of the science of mineralogy. It is for this reason that the finest and most complete polarizing microscopes are

* See polarizing accessories Chapter IX.

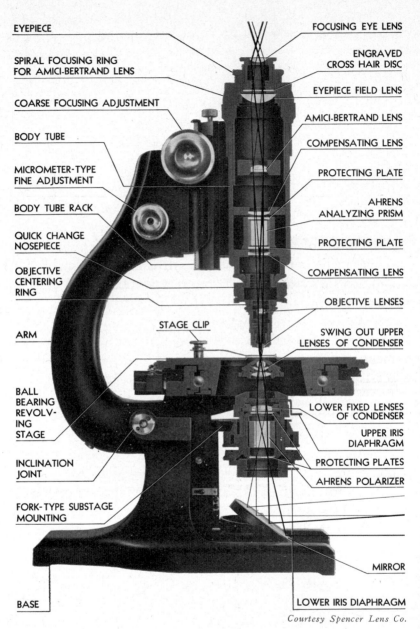

EYEPIECE

SPIRAL FOCUSING RING
FOR AMICI-BERTRAND LENS

COARSE FOCUSING ADJUSTMENT

BODY TUBE

MICROMETER-TYPE
FINE ADJUSTMENT

BODY TUBE RACK

QUICK CHANGE
NOSEPIECE

OBJECTIVE
CENTERING
RING

ARM

BALL
BEARING
REVOLV-
ING
STAGE

INCLINATION
JOINT

FORK-TYPE SUBSTAGE
MOUNTING

BASE

STAGE CLIP

FOCUSING EYE LENS

ENGRAVED
CROSS HAIR DISC

EYEPIECE FIELD LENS

AMICI-BERTRAND LENS

COMPENSATING LENS

PROTECTING PLATE

AHRENS
ANALYZING PRISM

PROTECTING PLATE

COMPENSATING LENS

OBJECTIVE LENSES

SWING OUT UPPER
LENSES OF CONDENSER

LOWER FIXED LENSES
OF CONDENSER

UPPER IRIS
DIAPHRAGM

PROTECTING PLATES

AHRENS POLARIZER

MIRROR

LOWER IRIS DIAPHRAGM

Courtesy Spencer Lens Co.

FIGURE 91

The petrographic polarizing microscope showing parts and the path of
light through the instrument.

called "Petrographic or Petrographical Microscopes." This simply means that the polarizing microscopes so called, have the additional accessories necessary for the proper observation of interference figures, etc.

The Polarizing microscope is used in many branches of science and industry. It has particularly valuable applications in the production of food products, textiles, ceramics, metals, petroleum, chemicals, papers, paints, varnishes and plastics. It is also a valuable aid in toxicology. For years it has been essential in geological and chemical research and for instruction and demonstrations in the laboratories of colleges and universities.

This type of microscope is very valuable where an understanding of the structure of materials affects final results or finished products. The characteristics which are usually identified are fibrous, granular, crystalline, powdered and colloidal.

In chemistry the use of polarizing microscopes is constantly increasing. As this occurs we find continual development in the science of chemical microscopy. A reaction created on a microscope slide and observed with a polarizing microscope often provides the chemist with a key to his subsequent procedure or with an actual analysis. It is also helpful as a means of estimating percentages of materials in solution.

We submit here a list of general uses in several fields of endeavor for the polarizing microscopes.*

1. Petroleum Geologists—(Petrographic Microscope).
   a—For the identification of heavy accessory minerals from various beds for purposes of correlation.

---

* The first item was suggested by Dr. Harry H. Hess of the Department of Geology at Princeton University. Items 2 to 9 inclusive have been published by Spencer Lens Company after careful analysis of the field. We are reproducing these items with their permission.

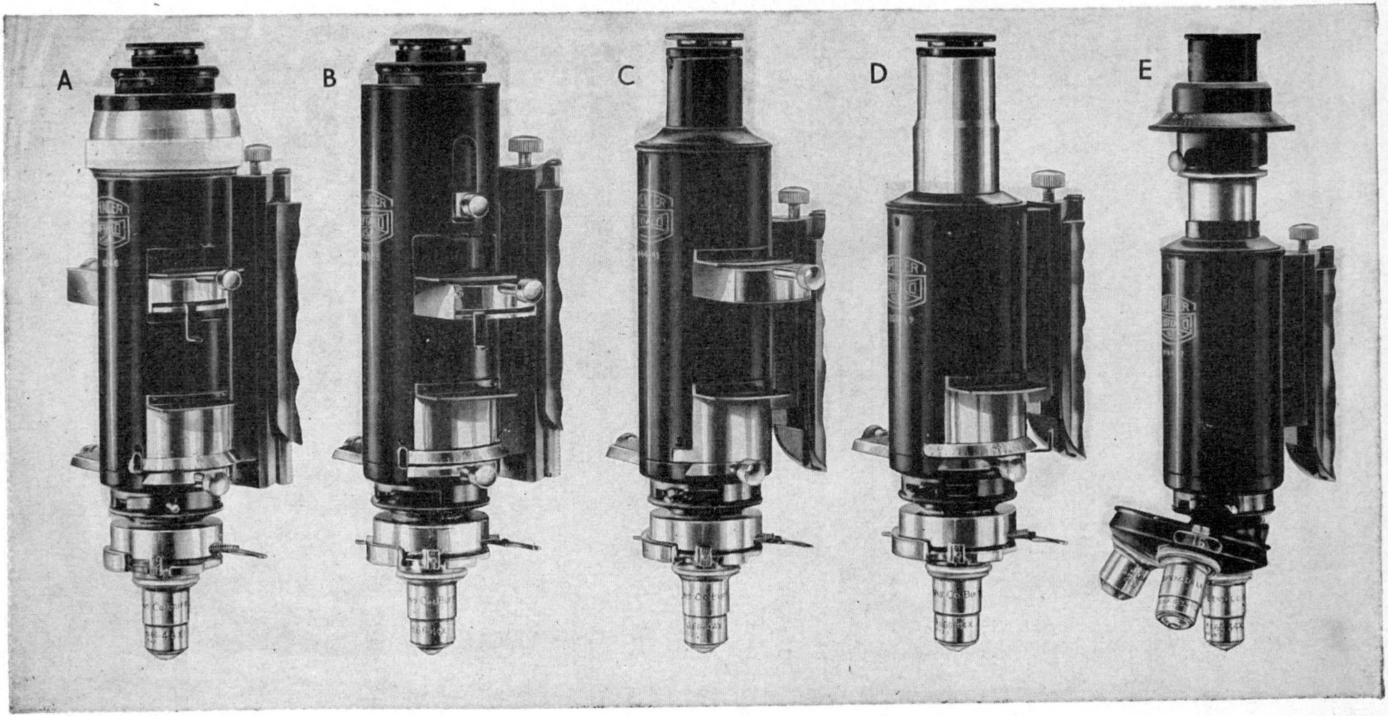

Courtesy Spencer Lens Co.

FIGURE 92

Tube equipments for polarizing microscopes: A—with spiral focusing mount for Bertrand lens. B—with sliding focusing mount for Bertrand lens. C—with stationary prefocused Bertrand lens. D—without Bertrand lens but with tube analyzer. E—without Bertrand lens—Cap Analyzer on top of tube.

b—To make accurate lithologic descriptions of samples from a well in order to correlate distinctive lithologic characters of certain horizons from well to well or from a well to surface outcrops.

c—Occasionally, for the examination of a thin section of a sediment to see how much pore space is present and what are the shapes of these spaces if any.

2. Medical

Many tissue components are optically active and the polarizing microscope is useful in the analysis of changes in the tissues during normal functioning or from pathological alteration. The detailed structure of protoplasm, nerve fiber and of the erythrocyte envelope may be investigated with this instrument. A considerable number of drugs and organic chemicals can be identified with the polarizing microscope which makes it useful in pharmacology, biological chemistry and toxicology. The location of inorganic material and its identification is facilitated when microincinerated preparations are examined with the polarizing microscope.

3. Ceramics

The development of crystalline material such as quartz, tridymite, cristobalite and mullite in most ceramic products may be examined with the polarizing microscope and control methods established. In the manufacture of glass it is being used in "trouble-shooting." For example: white spots or "stones" in the glass melt can be identified and their origin determined. The crystalline material in each case is different, easily identified, and often the trouble is quickly corrected. Polarized light is also useful in strain testing of bottles.

4. Mining

FIGURE 93

Substage assemblies for petrographic microscopes. Top of condenser may be swung out of the optic axis.

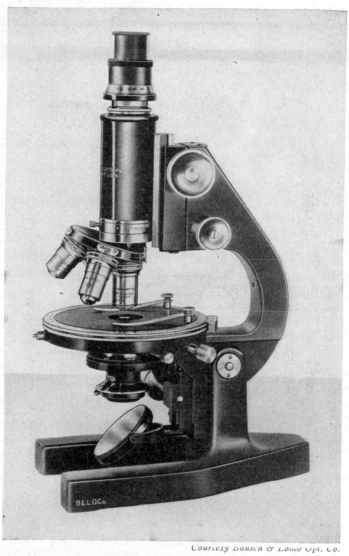

FIGURE 94

Chemical microscope with Cap Analyzer.

Mining engineers and geologists find a polarizing microscope an essential item of their laboratory equipment. They must identify the crystalline material, minerals and ores, in any particular locality, determine their value, and decide whether they are present in sufficient quantity to mine profitably. During mining operations, control tests are run frequently in order to be sure the material fulfills the requirements of the consumer.

5. Textile

In the textile industry the polarizing microscope is used to study and identify those natural and artificial fibers which exhibit definite optical characteristics. Silk and rayon manufacturers investigate the cross section, longitudinal striations, surface appearance and birefringence of fibers with the polarizing microscope.

6. Paper

Fibers in paper are studied in the same manner as textile. Impurities and contaminants are identified. The chemical and physical condition of the fibers is investigated after they have undergone certain manufacturing processes. Mineral fillers often reveal essential data when studied with the polarizing microscope.

7. Industrial Hygiene

The polarizing microscope is used in the identification of mineral dusts in industrial plants, and may supplement the laboratory microscope for particle size determination and dust counts.

8. Botanical

Another use of the polarizing microscope is the study of botanical fibers. Such fibers show definite optical properties and characteristics under polarized light. The investigation of cell wall structure and study of starches are important applications in this science.

FIGURE 95

Petrographic microscope for routine work,

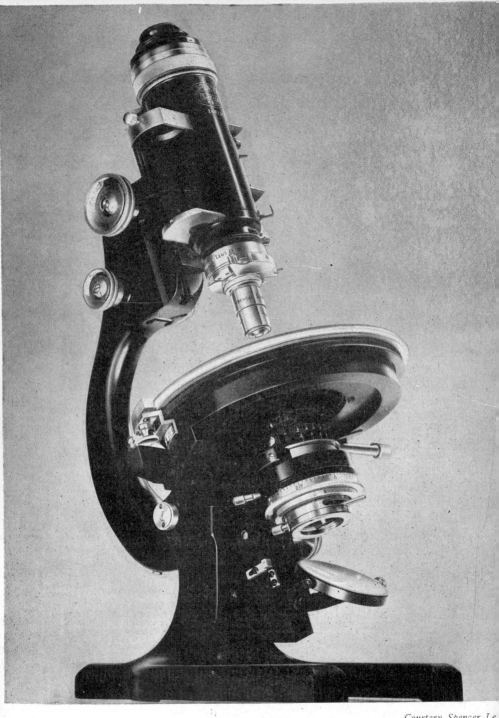

FIGURE 96

Research Petrographic microscope.

9. Food and Drugs

The analyst must frequently purify his material by recrystallization before identification can be made microscopically. Here the polarizing microscope proves to be a time saver, only minute amounts of material being necessary for precise analysis.

The crystalline substances thus identified, cover a wide range of materials, including:

a—Alkaloids and their salts (especially useful in drug analysis).

b—A large number of synthetic crystalline organic compounds (found in various medicinal formulae).

c—Inorganic substances used as fillers or active principles in various combinations.

d—Organic derivatives, crystalline in nature.

Non-crystalline, anisotropic materials, such as starches and fibers may be studied. Contaminants may be identified.

Miscellaneous crystalline material which often occurs in the course of a chemical analysis is sometimes present in such minute amounts that the usual test tube method of attack is unfavorable for correct identification. In that event the polarizing microscope is very useful in identifications, frequently furnishing only a portion of the picture, but giving complete confirmation to identify when other methods fail.

Polarized Light

Before proceeding with the construction and the actual use of a polarizing microscope, let us review polarized light and see what it does. This part of the chapter may be helpful to the student who has not been interested before in this phase of microscopy.

Ordinary light vibrates in all directions perpendicular to the direction in which it travels, whereas *polarized light* is forced to vibrate in only one direction. This

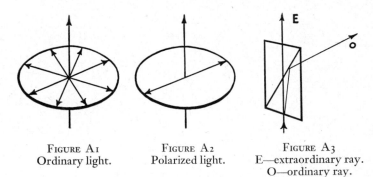

FIGURE A1
Ordinary light.

FIGURE A2
Polarized light.

FIGURE A3
E—extraordinary ray.
O—ordinary ray.

peculiarity of polarized light causes certain peculiar phenomena when passing through crystals, etc., which helps to identify them. Polarized light was first obtained with natural crystals such as tourmaline. Later other methods were developed such as the use of black glass reflectors and a patented sheet material called "Polaroid." * For microscopic work it was found that natural calcite crystals which were colorless and uniform could be so cut and mounted that they would polarize ordinary light perfectly. "Polaroid" film can also be used for this purpose, but *at this writing* the prisms are generally considered better.

As the light strikes the prism, it is split into two rays which are called the *ordinary* ray and the *extraordinary* ray. Each ray consists of 50% of the original light. The ordinary ray is totally reflected out of the field of

* A trade name for this material manufactured by the Polaroid Corporation.

view of the microscope when it hits the cemented surface of the prism. This is true whether the prism is
of the Nicol, Glan-Thompson, or Ahrens types. The

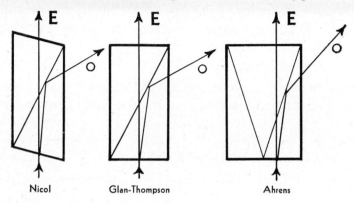

FIGURE A4

extraordinary ray continues straight through the prism
and emerges as polarized light.

The usual types of prisms used to obtain polarized
light are the Nicol, Glan-Thompson and Ahrens. Each
is cut in a different way. Many petrographers prefer
the Ahrens because it gives a large aperture and a large
field. However, the effect on ordinary light is the same
by each of these three prisms.

Construction of a Polarizing Microscope

Fig. 91 shows a complete polarizing microscope of
the petrographic type. As we see it has some additional parts in the optical system which are not found
in the conventional microscope. The stand is generally larger and heavier than the conventional microscope, and usually there is more space below the stage
to make room for additional substage parts. The stage
is circular and rotatable. It is graduated and equipped

with a vernier which generally can be read to 3 minutes of arc. In some instruments the rotation of the stage can be controlled also by means of a slow motion adjustment. This is very useful for research work and highly recommended although not necessary for routine work.

In modern polarizing microscopes the condenser is combined with the polarizing prism. This prism which goes under the condenser is called the "polarizer." Generally it can be rotated through 360 degrees and the amount of rotation checked. The condenser consists of two separate lens assemblies. The top assembly can be swung out of position so that when a low power objective is used its field can be properly illuminated. When higher power objectives are used both the lower and upper assemblies are generally used together. The polarizer itself can be removed from the condenser if it is desired to use the microscope without polarizing the light. The entire substage assembly can be focused up and down by means of a rack and pinion.

The tube, and equipment of same, in a polarizing microscope varies considerably. In fig. 91 we see that immediately above the objective there is a quick change receptacle which receives the centering ring into which the objective has been screwed. Above the receptacle the tube has a slot into which we can put our compensators such as the quartz wedge, selenite plate, mica plate, etc. Above the slot is one of the two compensating lenses which are mounted above and below the upper polarizing prism which is called an "analyzer." These are anastigmatizing lenses designed to provide constant magnification and focus as the "analyzer" (the upper polarizing prism referred to above) is moved in and out of the optical path. This analyzer is also protected against dust by protecting plates above and below its two exposed surfaces. They are necessary because when the analyzer is slid out of its effective position it would be exposed to dust if these protecting plates were not in position. The analyzer is carefully mounted between them, sometimes in a fixed position and sometimes so that it can be rotated through 90 or 100 degrees. The analyzer can be moved in and out of the optical path because it is mounted in a carefully fitted slideway.

Above the analyzer is found (in petrographic microscopes) the Amici Bertrand lens. It is usually called just "Bertrand lens." In the finest microscopes it is movable up and down so that it can be focused upon the back lens of the objective in use. Also, it is sometimes equipped with an iris diaphragm and a centering device. It also can be slid in and out of the optical path.

Finally there is the ocular in its usual position at the top of the tube. Since the tubes of polarizing microscopes vary in their diameter the eyepieces also vary. The large diameter tubes use larger eyepieces than the standard diameter tubes which use the standard diameter oculars. These latter oculars can be adapted to the larger tubes by using the necessary adapter which reduces the diameter of the top of the tube to the standard opening. Naturally the large diameter oculars give a larger field of view than the smaller ones. This also makes it necessary to mount in the tube a larger analyzer prism. Microscopes with large diameter tubes are more expensive mainly because of this larger analyzer.

In polarizing microscopes the eyepieces also differ

from the standard oculars in that they always have a cross hair mounted in them. One of the lines of the cross hair goes directly away from the worker and the other is perpendicular to the first one. Also the eye (top) lens of the ocular is focusable up and down in some manner so that any person can get in perfect focus simultaneously both the object under observation and the crosshairs. This is necessary because of the difference in focus of the eyes of different people.

Now we come to a very important point. *In polarizing microscopes the objectives must be mounted so that they are free of strain.* A little strain developed in the mounting of regular objectives does not affect their efficiency provided the strain is not serious, but in polarizing microscopes it is a *very serious* matter. If there is strain in the objectives this will affect our conclusions in examining a specimen. We may get the wrong results for the strain will rotate the polarized light. Therefore, *never use objectives which are not free of strain for exact work with polarized light.* The objectives sold by reputable manufacturers for use with polarizing microscopes are always strain free.

This is one of the reasons why a standard conventional microscope is not very good for exact work with polarized light. Its objectives may have a little strain. Naturally strain free objectives are usually more expensive than the regular objectives.

Let us summarize the optical parts of a complete polarizing microscope. The optical train consists of:

a—Substage assembly consisting of the rotatable graduated polarizer combined with the condenser.

b—*Strain free* objective.

c—A compensator (if one is used) such as a quartz wedge.

d—The analyzer which may or may not be rotatable.

e—The Bertrand lens which may or may not be focusable.

f—The ocular with its crosshair disc and focusable eye lens.

Fig. 92 which shows the usual variations in tube equipment is self explanatory. When the careful study of magnified interference figures is not necessary there is no reason to have a Bertrand lens and it is therefore eliminated from some polarizing microscopes. Also, in such cases, the cost of the microscope may be reduced by using the analyzer on top of the ocular instead of in the tube of the microscope. This reduces the field of view to some extent, but the action of polarized light can be observed.

In a good polarizing microscope the rotatable polarizer should be so mounted and graduated, that when it is set at zero its vibration direction is set at 90 degrees to that of the analyzer. At zero therefore we should have crossed prisms and none of the light should reach our eye unless an optically active material is being observed. In such a case, the object rotates the plane of polarization and therefore appears bright or colored on a black background. If the analyzer is also rotatable (either the tube or the top type) it should be also so mounted and graduated that when both the analyzer and polarizer are set at zero the crossed prisms condition is attained.

How Polarized Light Works in a Polarizing Microscope

When ordinary light is directed from the mirror to the polarizer it emerges from the polarizer as polarized

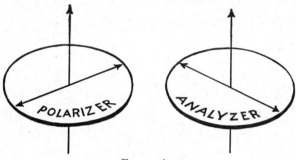

FIGURE A5

light. It passes on through the optical system to the analyzer. Since the vibration direction of the analyzer is set at 90 degrees to that of the polarizer none of the light which reaches the analyzer is allowed to pass to the eye. The extraordinary ray coming from the polarizer has become the ordinary ray of the analyzer and it is therefore reflected out of the field of the microscope. The field appears black, unless, as we pointed out before, an object which rotates the plane of polarization interferes, with the natural path of the light. This peculiarity of the polarizing microscope is what makes it so valuable for analysis of many materials.

Preparation of Crystalline Material

Some crystalline materials are already in convenient form for identification with a polarizing microscope, others must be prepared.

A representative example of solid crystalline material, such as a geological or mineralogical specimen, must be crushed in a diamond steel mortar. This breaks the mass into fine crystals which are then selected by screening through a 100 mesh onto a 200 mesh screen. These screens are small, 3 or 4 inches in diameter.

A comparatively small number of the selected crystals are mounted in a liquid of known refractive index on a glass slide. The liquids commonly used in making up a set of known refractive indices are water, kerosene, glycerine, cedar oil, clove oil, cassia oil, and methylene iodide. The index of refraction of two oils mixed together is measured with a "refractometer." The usual procedure in mounting is to place one or two drops of the oil in the center of a glass slide, and to tap the crystals into the oil from the end of a small blade or spatula. Care should be taken not to clutter the field with crystals because this is confusing when ascertaining correct optical properties. A cover glass is then placed over the crystals. The sample is now properly mounted for microscopic examination.

The preparation of massive crystalline specimens in thin sections for examination under polarized light is a more difficult task. It is necessary to grind one surface perfectly flat, mount the specimen on the glass slide in melted balsam, and then grind the other rough side until the sample is thin enough to permit light to pass through it. Petrologists generally work to a final thickness of about 30 microns. However those interested in obtaining the most brilliantly polarizing rock sections use a thickness of about 50 or 60 microns. Materials such as quartz and feldspar then give better colors.

This grinding technique is difficult to master. It requires considerable patience and should be learned if possible under the supervision of an experienced worker. If this is not possible prepared rock sections of many types can be purchased for examination. There are several dealers in microscopical slides who sell them. Usually three or more grades of carborundum are used in the hand grinding operation, the finest being No. 600. After grinding is completed a little Canada Balsam is melted on top of the specimen and a cover glass pressed carefully on top of the balsam. The result is a permanently mounted thin section suitable for examination.

Procedure for Adjusting Polarizing Microscopes

Before a polarizing microscope can be used to advantage we must make sure that all its parts are in perfect adjustment. We suggest the following procedure. Where necessary we shall comment on the various steps as each applies to the average user of polarizing microscopes. This procedure covers the testing of a "petrographic" microscope. These instruments may get out of adjustment in transit when they are shipped or when they are used improperly by students. To make a complete test the following slides are recommended.

1. Stage micrometer. (See Chapter IX. Optical measuring accessories.)
2. Thick quartz section.
3. Bichloride of Mercury crystals.
4. Thin quartz section.

Proceed as follows:

1. Center the objectives—The objectives on petrographic microscopes must be accurately centered. When the objectives are changed the center of the

cross hairs in the ocular must fall near the same place or spot as in the previous case. Use the stage micrometer, 10X ocular and start the centering with the 16mm objective. Move the stage micrometer until the center of the cross hair lies within one of the zeros. Rotate the stage and observe whether or not the center of the cross hairs remains within the o. If necessary the centering screws of the centering objective ring are used to bring about this condition. Let us suppose that as the stage is rotated the o moves downward and outward on the cross hairs instead of rotating within itself. We rotate the stage until the o reaches its lowest position before it starts going up again toward the center of the cross hairs on the other side of the vertical cross hair line. Using the centering screws we move its image right up this vertical line *half way to the center of the cross*

FIGURE A6

Cross hairs superimposed over image
of stage micrometer.

hairs, not all the way. Then, we move the slide itself very carefully until the o is where it should be, right in the center of the cross hairs. If we have done this correctly, as we rotate the stage the o will stay in the center and rotate within itself. Now we have both our 16mm objective and our test object properly centered. With patient and careful manipulation of the centering screws and the slide this condition can be reached. Now, we must not touch the slide again, the centering of the other objectives must be done *only with the centering screws* of their respective centering rings. Next, center the highest power objective *and without moving the slide,* except for the rotation of the stage, center all other objectives to the same point.

2. Eyepieces—Check the centering of the eyepieces while the stage micrometer slide is still on the stage of the microscope. Use the 16mm objective. The eyepieces should be centered within about 0.01mm and the cross hairs of all eyepieces must be parallel. Eyepieces are carefully selected and inspected at the factory and usually have no means for adjustment in the field.

3. Bertrand Lens—The Bertrand lens must be checked for clear focus and centering. Place the thick

FIGURE A7

Quartz interference figure.

quartz section on the stage; open all the way *both condenser* diaphragms; * swing into position the upper condensing lens; use the centered 4mm objective; insert the analyzer at its zero position so that the field appears black (if the field does not appear black when both the analyzer and the polarizer are set at 0, then it is

* If there are two.

possible that one or the other is out of adjustment, in that case, rotate one or the other anyway until the field appears black); throw in the Bertrand lens by sliding it into the tube of the microscope. Now focus the Bertrand lens on the interference figure which appears on the back lens of the objective. Naturally the objective has been focused to a point very close, almost touching the slide on the stage of the microscope. The Bertrand lens thus acts as an objective, and the back lens of the real microscope objective becomes the object. The pattern of the interference figure seen should appear as sharp colored concentric rings with a large black cross passing through the center of the field. If the Bertrand lens is focusable move it up and down until the interference figure is sharpest. The center of the figure should lie at the exact center of the cross hairs of the eyepiece. If this is not the case, and if the Bertrand lens has centering screws, it can be centered to the ideal position.

4. Check the Centering of the Substage—The substage condenser mount must be accurately centered in order to have the entire optical system in perfect alignment. a, Remove the slide from the stage of the microscope and use the 4mm objective, 10X ocular, the analyzer and the Bertrand lens. Be sure that the analyzer is set at 0 and rotate the polarizer about 35 degrees off zero to allow a certain amount of light to pass through the system. If the Bertrand lens has an iris close it as much as possible. Swing out the upper condenser, close the upper diaphragm of the condenser and focus carefully on this diaphragm. If it is not centered it is necessary to use the provision made by the manufacturer to do so (this is not easy in the field, usually it means

the use of a fine screw driver to operate the small centering screws which generally move the entire substage in its ring. This is done by careful and patient manipulation of these screws one against the other). b, Open the upper iris of the condenser and close the lower one. The image of the lower iris should remain in position when the polarizer is rotated. If it shifts it is not centered. It is necessary to do so by the means provided by the manufacturer (this is also quite tricky, usually there are three little screws on the under side of the polarizer which must be loosened so that the diaphragm can be moved until it is properly centered. When the screws are tightened the diaphragm may move slightly. It is best then to do any further centering with the three adjusting screws which usually move the lower lens of the condenser). c, Swing in the upper condenser, open the lower iris diaphragm and close the upper one. Note the position of the image of this diaphragm. If it is not centered, use the three screws usually found on the side of the cell mount to bring it into proper position (this is also difficult, it takes patience to do it properly). The complete substage is now accurately centered. Usually none of all this is necessary but the centering should be checked and if it is out we know now how to take care of it.

5. Proper Setting of Polarizer—Only in rare cases does the polarizer get out of adjustment. However, this procedure is valuable as a check. Place a slide of bichloride of mercury crystals on the stage, use the 16mm objective, and the 10X eyepiece. Swing out the upper lens of the condenser. Select a straight, elongated crystal and make this crystal coincide with the vertical cross hair of the eyepiece. Use both the polarizer and

the analyzer setting each at zero. The crystal should appear black, or practically invisible in the field of the microscope. If it appears light rotate the polarizer until the crystal becomes dark. The polarizer is off its set zero point by that number of degrees. In such case it

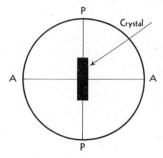

FIGURE A8

must be turned in its mount so that the scale reads zero when the crystal is lined up with the cross hair, and is dark.

6. Analyzer Setting—The analyzer may possibly get out of adjustment and should be set in the proper relationship to the polarizer. Remove both the objective and the eyepiece, swing out the upper condenser and insert the analyzer into the body tube. Set the polarizer at zero and rotate the analyzer (if it is rotatable) until the field appears black. The analyzer is correctly set if this maximum darkness results when it is set at zero. The slightest movement of the analyzer off zero should cause the field to become brighter. If the analyzer is off, it must be rotated in its mount till the proper relationship exists.

Important. Obviously, test 5 may be affected by the position of the analyzer, and test 6 by the position of the polarizer. Also, if by any chance the objectives

used are not strain free, both tests would be valueless
for the analyzer and the polarizer settings. Furthermore, the turning of the prisms in their mounts is difficult. It is therefore recommended that, if tests 5 and
6 show maladjustment of the parts in question, the microscope be sent back to the factory for proper adjustment.

We now proceed with the tests for the usual compensators.

7. Selenite Plate—It is a simple matter to check the
orientation of the selenite plate. Place the thin quartz
section on the stage, use the 4mm objective, 10X eye-

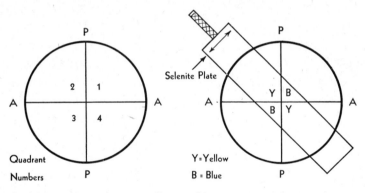

FIGURE A9

piece, Bertrand lens, analyzer and polarizer set at zero
and the upper condenser lens in place. Insert the selenite plate in the slot for compensators. Check to see
that the arrow engraved on the plate is in the direction
in fig. A9. If this is true, yellow spots should appear
near the center of the cross in quadrants 2 and 4.

8. Mica Plate—Remove the selenite plate and insert
the mica plate. Check the plate to see that the arrow
is engraved as indicated. Two black dots should appear

in the 2 and 4 quadrants. A line joining these dots would make a 45 degree angle with the cross hairs.

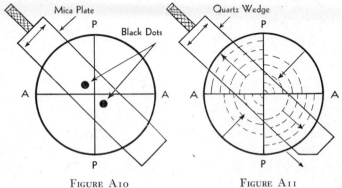

FIGURE A10   FIGURE A11

9. Quartz Wedge—To check the quartz wedge, remove the thin quartz section from the stage and replace it with the thick quartz section. Insert the wedge in the slot *thin edge first,* the arrow on the wedge marking the thick end. As the wedge is inserted the color curves should shift outward in the 2 and 4 quadrants and contract toward the center in the 1 and 3 quadrants.

The direction of the arrow on the above mentioned three accessories marks the direction of vibration of the slow ray of the plate.

Crystals and Their Optical Classification

The most important use of polarized light at the present time is the identification of crystalline material. The following gives a brief description of the optical properties of crystals which make possible their identification with a polarizing microscope.

A crystal is a solid body whose physical properties result from the arrangement of atoms into a definite geometric form, such as cube, hexagon or rhombohedron. Precipitation, vaporization, fusion and changes in the solid state are the common methods of obtaining crystals.

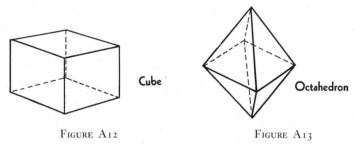

FIGURE A12   FIGURE A13

They are generally classified under six systems. However, we are more interested in optical classification because each crystal has a set of optical properties which make its identification possible. The optical classification divides crystals into three groups:

1. Isoaxial (Isotropic)
2. Uniaxial ⎫
3. Biaxial ⎬ (Anisotropic)
           ⎭

Isotropic is a term used to describe material that shows no optical properties or is invisible when observed between crossed prisms. Light travels through this material at the same speed regardless of the direction that it passed through the crystal.

Anisotropic refers to material which appears alternately bright and dark when rotated between crossed prisms. Light travels through this material at different speeds, depending on the direction that it passes through the crystal.

1. Isoaxial: Such materials as powdered glass not under strain, transparent substances and certain crystals

are isoaxial, because light travels through them in all directions at the same speed. They are invisible between crossed prisms. These isoaxial crystals are identified by determining their one refractive index by the Becke Line Method. This is explained later.

2. Uniaxial crystals: In uniaxial crystals light travels at a definite speed when parallel to one axis. At an angle to this axis the speed is different. These crystals are anisotropic, appearing alternately bright and dark when observed between crossed prisms. They have two refractive indices. Quartz crystals, starch grains and fused sodium nitrate are a few uniaxial substances. Uniaxial material may be quickly identified by inserting the Bertrand lens and observing a very definite pattern called an interference figure in the field of the microscope.

A large black cross appears on the center of the field with colored concentric circles preceding outward from the center. Information about the specific properties to be determined from this figure and the use of accessories will be included later.

Biaxial Crystals: In biaxial crystals, light travels at different speeds in the direction of the two axes. These crystals are anisotropic and have three indices of refraction which are determined by the Becke Line Method. Boric acid, sulphonal, Topaz and Kyanite are

FIGURE A14	FIGURE A15	FIGURE A16	FIGURE A17
Uniaxial optic axis figure.	Biaxial optic axis figure.	Acute Bisectrix.	Obtuse Bisectrix.

a few biaxial materials. These crystals have several characteristic interference figures which are observed by using the Bertrand Lens and crossed prisms.

It is not possible to explain the theory of these characteristic figures here. However, one of these figures will be observed depending upon how the crystal is crushed with reference to its optic axes.

This method of classifying crystals is used by all chemical microscopists, metallurgists and petrographers who actually identify unknown materials. The chemical microscopist sometimes is more interested in the presence of crystals rather than in their identification. The polarizing light feature is all that is necessary for making this observation. This is the reason why *chemical microscopes* are not usually equipped with a Bertrand Lens.

It is quite impossible to enter here upon a completely scientific explanation of all the optical characteristics of crystals. However, the main optical properties of crystals, as investigated by petrographers and, in some cases, chemical microscopists, will be described now.

Explanation of Optical Characteristics

The properties are:

1. Optical Classification *
   (Isoxial, Uniaxial, Biaxial)
2. Refractive Index
3. Optic Sign
4. Sign of Elongation
5. Optic Axial Angle
6. Extinction Angle

* Discussed in the preceding paragraphs.

7. Birefringence

8. Pleochroism

Refractive Index. Refractive index is a measure of the refraction or bending of light rays as they pass, at

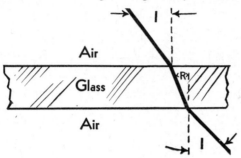

FIGURE A18

R = Angle of refracted ray.
I = Angle of Incident ray.

an oblique angle, from one medium to another, for example glass to air, air to water.

Mathematically, the refractive index is equal to the sine of the angle of incidence over the sine of the angle of refraction.

$$\text{Index of Refraction} = \frac{\text{Sine I}}{\text{Sine R}}$$

The indices of refraction of a few common substances are:

Air 1.000	Canada Balsam 1.544
Water 1.336	Quartz 1.547
Clove Oil 1.530	Methylene Iodide 1.740

Becke Line Method: In crystal analysis the index of refraction is determined by the Becke Line Method. The crystals are immersed in oil on a microscope slide and a concentrated bright line appears around the edge of the specimen. As the body tube of the microscope is slowly raised the bright line shifts toward the medium of higher refractive index; either the oil or the crystal. By trial and error method an oil will be found in which the crystal disappears. (A similar condition exists when a glass rod is immersed in a bottle of cedar wood oil.) The index of refraction of the specimen is recorded as the index of the oil which is known (the index of the oil can be measured with a refractometer).

Optic Sign: To explain the optic sign of a crystal it is necessary to recall the fact that light is split into two rays traveling at different speeds when it strikes certain crystals. One of these rays is called the ordinary ray (O) and the other the extraordinary ray (E). When the ordinary ray travels faster than the extraordinary, the crystal is positive, when the opposite is true, the crystal is negative. In practice the quartz wedge, selenite plate or mica plate may be used to determine the optic sign of the crystal.

Sign of Elongation: Many minerals and crystal specimens are elongated along one axis and appear like long

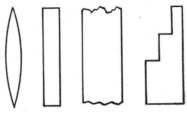

FIGURE A19

needles or rectangles. Some of these shapes may be illustrated as in Fig. A19. The axis along which the crystal is elongated will determine its sign of elongation, positive or negative. The selenite plate or mica plate may be used for this determination. Further information appears later.

Optic Axial Angle: The term optic axial angle refers to biaxial crystals only and is an important factor in the identification of these crystals. The optic axial angle

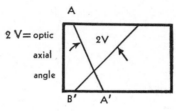

FIGURE A20

is the angle between the rays of light which follow the two optic axes of the biaxial crystals, this characteristic is denoted as $2V$ in the description tables, for instance $2V = 14°$.

Extinction Angle: Uniaxial and biaxial crystals are extinct for certain positions under the microscope when observed between crossed prisms. The angle through which a crystal must be rotated from a position parallel with a cross hair to its extinction position, is its extinction angle. This is measured by reading the vernier on the rotating stage.

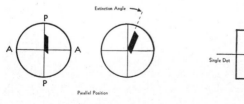

FIGURE A21

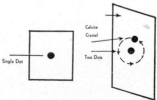

FIGURE A22

Birefringence: Birefringence is the property of a crystal to separate the two rays of light resulting from the original single ray of ordinary light, that is, the ordinary and extraordinary ray. A crystal of calcite may be used to demonstrate this phenomena. By placing the calcite crystal over a single dot, two dots will be observed. As the crystal is rotated, one dot will remain stationary and the other will rotate around it. The stationary dot is the ordinary ray, the other is the extraordinary ray. This phenomena is also called double refraction.

The difference between the index of refraction of the ordinary and the extraordinary ray of the crystal is a quantitative measure of its birefringence. For example:

Crystals	Difference between indices	Birefringence
Cerussite	.273	strong
Quartz	.009	weak

Pleochroism: Pleochroism is the property of certain crystals to absorb some wave lengths of light more than others regardless of optical characteristics. This results in a variation in the natural color of the crystal as it is rotated under the microscope *with the analyzer removed from the optical path.*

The Use of the Polarizing Microscope for the Identification of Crystalline Material

In order to determine the optical characteristics of crystals, use a good microscope lamp which gives plenty of light and illumination A (Chapter III). Then, the following steps are recommended:

1. *Optical Classifications:* The crystals should be placed between crossed prisms, upper condenser swung out and a 32 or 16mm objective in position. If no color appears as the stage is rotated, the material is said to be *isotropic*. However, if color does appear in the black field, the crystals are said to be *anisotropic*.

Isotropic crystals are identified by throwing out the analyzer and using a 16 or 4mm objective. This shows the crystal in plane polarized light and the index of refraction is measured by the Becke Line method.

In classifying Anisotropic crystals as uniaxial or biaxial, it is necessary to swing in the upper condenser, insert the analyzer and the Bertrand lens, and use an 8, 4 or 1.8mm objective. The crystal must be brought directly under the cross hair to obtain the proper interference figure. A uniaxial figure appears to be a black cross or a set of concentric colored circles with a black cross in the center of the field. A biaxial figure consists of oval rings around two dark spots, the field being crossed by two hyperbolas as the stage is rotated.

2. *Refractive Index:* The refractive index of anisotropic crystals is determined by the Becke Line method. Uniaxial crystals have two indices, biaxial have three indices. For precise determination of refractive indices, a universal stage may be used. This accessory makes it possible to orient the crystal with respect to its axis and eliminates searching for a properly oriented crystal.

3. *Optical Sign:* The optical sign of a uniaxial crystal may be determined by throwing in upper condenser, analyzer and Bertrand lens, and using either the quartz wedge, quarter wave plate or selenite plate in the slot for compensators. When the quartz wedge is used, the direction in which the color curves move out-

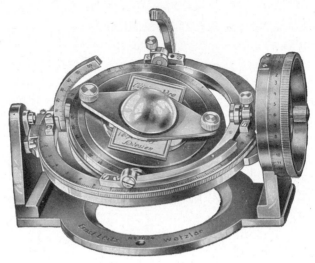

FIGURE 97

Universal Rotating Stage.

ward on inserting the wedge makes the sign with the slow ray of the wedge as indicated by the arrow.

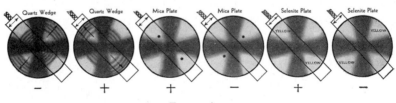

FIGURE A23

When the quarter wave (mica) plate is used, the line joining the two black dots will be parallel to the slow ray of the plate as indicated by the arrow if the crystal is negative. The line joining the dots is at right angles to the arrow if the crystal is positive.

When the selenite plate is used, the line joining the quadrants in which the yellow color appears shows the sign in the same manner as above.

The determination of the sign of biaxial crystals depends upon several other considerations which are too involved to be presented here.*

4. *Sign of Elongation:* The analyzer should be thrown in and a 16 or 4mm objective used. The "first order red" plate (selenite) is inserted in the slot for compensators and the center of the crystals is set at the center of the cross hairs. Then the crystal is rotated until its elongated axis is parallel with the arrow on the plate. If the crystal appears yellow, its sign of elongation is negative. If it appears blue, the sign of elongation is positive.

5. *Optic Axial Angle:* The optic axial angle of biaxial crystals is observed by throwing in the upper condenser, analyzer and Bertrand lens. A quantitative measure of this angle may be obtained by using an apertometer plate in the condenser, a coordinate grating in a special eyepiece, or an objective with a calibrated iris diaphragm.

6. *Extinction Angle:* The extinction angle is measured by throwing in the analyzer and rotating the crystal from a position parallel with the cross hairs until

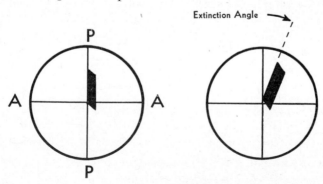

Parallel Position

FIGURE A24

* "Elements of Optical Mineralogy," Book 1 by A. N. Winchell.

it appears black. The degree of rotation is determined by reading the vernier scale on the circular stage.

7. *Birefringence:* Birefringence may be measured by means of a graduated quartz wedge and by referring to Newton's color scale or Levy's chart.

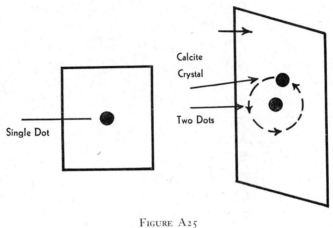

FIGURE A25
Birefringence.

8. *Pleochroism:* The upper condenser and analyzer should be thrown out to determine pleochroism. If the crystal exhibits two extremes of color as it is rotated, it is called dichroic; three, trichroic.

Use of the Petrographic Microscope When Accessories Used Make It Impossible to Rotate the Stage

For certain work and under certain conditions it is necessary to keep the stage in a definite position. It cannot be rotated. When this is the case it is necessary to rotate synchronously the two polarizing prisms—the analyzer and the polarizer. In order to do this a special petrographic microscope is necessary. The analyzer and the polarizer are connected by a device which makes this possible. Such an instrument is illustrated in fig. 98. In this instrument the synchronous rotation of the nicols extends to 240 degrees in all positions of the tube and illuminating apparatus, and has a device for locking the rotation and setting the stage in the normal

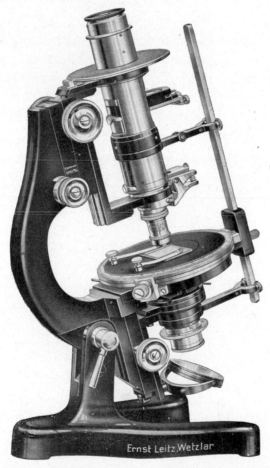

Courtesy E. Leitz, Inc.

FIGURE 98

Research petrographic microscope with provision for synchronous rotation of polarizer and analyzer.

and diagonal positions, respectively. The tube analyzer and the "Amici-Bertrand" lens can be inserted and withdrawn in any position of the synchronous rotation of the nicols, and the cross lines in the eyepiece remain set parallel and at right angles to the direction of vibration in all phases of the rotation, likewise also during the operation of synchronous rotation. The compensators retain their diagonal position with reference to the directions of vibrations while synchronous rotation takes place. The polarizer and analyzer may be separately rotated through an angle of 240 degrees, the amount of the rotation can be read by verniers to 0.1 degrees from either scale at the stage or tube.

CHAPTER IX

ACCESSORIES FOR THE MICROSCOPE

VERY often the use of the proper accessory will help to solve a difficult problem in microscopy which otherwise would be baffling.

Several accessories have been mentioned in the previous pages. Among them are the vertical illuminators, the condensers for light and dark fields, the various microscope lamps, etc. Here we shall list and illustrate when possible many other useful accessories. Their proper use will be explained.

There are so many accessories available that it is impossible to list them all, furthermore, many of them are so highly specialized that they are of no interest to the great majority of microscopists. Those listed here are accessories used quite generally and should be of interest to anybody who uses a microscope. Accessories which have been discussed previously will not be listed here unless they are studied from a different point of view.

Objectives and Oculars

Although we have discussed objectives and oculars all through the book, this has been done as important and integral parts of the microscope. The following condensed suggestions may prove helpful.

Oculars: Wide field oculars (which usually have a higher eyepoint than the standard huyghenian) are very helpful if one must wear glasses when working with the microscope. By using them when glasses are worn, the

Courtesy Spencer Lens

FIGURE 99

Objectives and Oculars—The second objective (from left) is a "stirrup" objective.

field of view obtained is about the same as that available when regular huyghenian oculars are used without glasses.

High eyepoint compensating oculars are available (and they are very helpful) for use with eyeglasses.

The special photomicrographic oculars are very helpful when taking photomicrographs. Many microscope manufacturers make them and call them by different trade names.

Objectives: Whenever possible it is a good idea to purchase the oil immersion objective equipped with an iris diaphragm. This saves considerable time and trouble if a dark field condenser is used often.

"Stirrup" or "Bifocus" 16mm objectives are available to change quickly from a 10x initial magnification to 4x. This is accomplished by swinging out of position the lower lens mount of the objective which is mounted on a sort of swinging stirrup. It must be remembered however that the 4x magnification thus obtained usually is not as good (in definition) as that of a standard 4x (32mm) objective. The 10x is just the same as the standard because the divisible 10x lenses are primarily designed for this magnification. The same is often true with the modern standard 16mm 10x achromatic objectives. The lower lenses of these objectives can be unscrewed and the remaining lens gives a magnification of 4x. The only difference is that in the "stirrup" objectives the change from one magnification to the other can be made more rapidly and easier.

Measuring and Counting Accessories

These accessories are very important, for without them, it is very difficult if not impossible to measure with a microscope the exact size of a minute object. The usual measuring "set" consists of a micrometer glass disc 21.15 or 21.13mm in diameter which is placed in the ocular, *and a stage micrometer slide used to calibrate the real value of the scale on the disc.* The stage micrometer usually has a 2mm scale divided to .01mm or a 0.2″ long scale graduated to .001 of an inch.

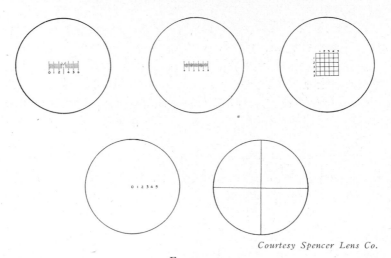

FIGURE 100

Measuring and counting ocular discs.

There are many types of micrometer measuring and counting discs with rulings more or less fine. Some are designed for special purposes. The usual ones have a 5mm scale divided into 50 parts to 0.1mm or into 100 parts to .05mm. This does not mean however that we can measure a microscopic object with this disc simply by putting it in the ocular. We must calibrate it to establish the real value of the graduations for the magnification used because the scale of the disc is purely arbitrary. We shall explain this calibration later.

There are also the following discs which are used quite generally:

The "Howard" disc for mold counting. It is ruled in squares for use with the usual 10x huyghenian ocular. Each square has an area equal to one-sixth of the diameter of the field of view. These discs are used with the Howard mold counting chamber which receives the material to be examined and counted. It is generally employed for the determination of the mold count of food products.

The "Whipple" disc is used for counting bacteria and dust particles. It has a large square subdivided into 4 smaller ones, each of which in turn is subdivided into 25 smaller squares. One of these smaller squares is further subdivided into 25 more squares.

"Milk Smear" disc for the counting of bacteria in milk smears. Has an 8.0mm diameter circle with cross lines dividing it into quadrants for easy and accurate counting.*

"Net" disc—usually a 5mm square divided into millimeter or .5 millimeter squares. Used for counting fairly large materials such as the coarser abrasives.

"Finder" disc—is numbered from center out 1, 2, 3, 4, 5, equally spaced. Very useful to call another person's attention to a particular part of the field. The specimen is moved so that the part in question is under one of the numbers and thus located; or the ocular rotated so that one of the numbers is over the desired part.

"Cross hair" disc, which divides the field into quadrants. Often used for measuring larger objects with a mechanical stage and for use with polarizing accessories.

The discs designed for use inside the ocular are placed in position in a huyghenian eyepiece, and in some compensating oculars, in the following manner: The top lens assembly of the ocular is unscrewed from the tube

* "Counting bacteria by means of the microscope"—Robert S. Breed and James D. Brew, circular #58—N. Y. State Exp. Station, Geneva, N. Y.

of the eyepiece and the disc is placed *face down* on the diaphragm. Then the top lens is screwed back in position. If this is done correctly, and if the diaphragm of the ocular is in the proper position for the individual's eye, then the scale or ruling can be seen in perfect focus over the specimen. If this is not the case either the disc was placed upside down or the diaphragm of the ocular has to be moved up or down slightly. To determine this it is necessary to unscrew the top lens of the ocular a little while the specimen under observation is in focus; if the ruling comes into focus, then the diaphragm must be moved down some; if it does not come into focus the diaphragm must be moved up. Naturally in either case, after the adjustment is made the top lens of the ocular is turned back firmly into place.

People who have average vision generally do not have to do the above but the eyes of some workers require the adjustment of the position of the diaphragm for the best results. To eliminate this troublesome operation, the *micrometer eyepieces* were developed. They are huyghenian oculars having the eye lens made focusable by spiral action so that the micrometer scale can be brought into sharp focus for any eye. The best are those in which the micrometer disc in the eyepiece is so mounted that it can be removed quickly and easily for cleaning. It is sometimes possible to order one of these micrometer eyepieces equipped with one of the special discs instead of with the standard measuring discs with which they are generally sold. This however usually means a special factory job and the cost of the eyepiece so equipped is likely to be much higher.

The Screw Micrometer and the Filar Micrometer Eyepieces

These eyepieces are very similar but they operate somewhat differently. They are used in the microscope, in place of the regular ocular, for making very exact measurements. They both have focusable eye lenses.

Courtesy Spencer Lens Co.

FIGURE 101

Screw micrometer eyepiece.

Before using they must be calibrated. In the Screw Micrometer Eyepiece the scale (which is purely an arbitrary ruling) is movable by means of a graduated drum. The center of the scale is a V which serves as a reference point for the scale. Each interval in the scale is exactly equivalent to one revolution of the screw which moves it; fractions of a revolution are indicated by the drum which is graduated into 100 parts. In measuring the length of an object, the scale is moved until one of the lines coincides with the margin of the

FIGURE 102

Filar micrometer eyepiece.

object under examination; then, by noting the amount of revolution necessary to bring another line into coincidence with the opposite side, the fractional part of the last division can be read to hundredths. The scale has thirty divisions and the real value of these must be established for each objective used. These screw micrometers are particularly useful for exact measurements of large objects because it is not necessary to move a cross hair over the entire length of the object.

For the measurement of very small objects many workers prefer the Filar Micrometer Eyepiece. This eyepiece also has a screw micrometer actuated by a drum divided into 100 parts. The drum however moves a cross hair across the field instead of a scale. One revolution of the drum moves the cross hair 1mm across the field, therefore each space on the drum equals 0.01mm. Estimations can easily be made to .001mm. A fine line running through the center of the field parallel to the axis of the screw serves as a guide in orienting the object with reference to the direction of motion of the movable cross hair. A scale in the field ruled in intervals of 0.5mm serves for counting the revolutions of the screw. Naturally for an exact measurement the real value of the movement of the cross hair and drum must be determined for each objective used with a stage micrometer.

Method of Calibrating Micrometer Discs for Eyepieces and Measurement of Small Objects

All of the scales placed in the eyepieces have arbitrary length and the apparent length depends on the magnification. Consequently, each scale has to be calibrated for use *with each combination of objective and eyepiece.* To do this the stage micrometer slide previously mentioned is necessary.

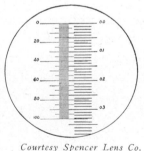

Courtesy Spencer Lens Co.

FIGURE 103

Calibration of micrometer disc.

To calibrate, focus on the stage micrometer and move it until the zero line corresponds exactly with the zero line of the micrometer disc. Always use as many divisions as possible.

The true distance (x) seen on the stage micrometer

which corresponds to the number of divisions (y) of the eyepiece disc is then noted. If we now divide the true distance by the number of divisions of the eyepiece disc, we find the distance each one takes in which is called the calibration constant or reduction factor (c). Thus we have $c=x/y$.

The number of divisions of the micrometer disc necessary to cover the specimen multiplied by the calibration constant (c) gives us the true length of the object. Therefore, the calibration in fig. 103 which shows us 100 divisions of the eyepiece disc taking in 33 divisions of the stage micrometer, would give us .33mm/100 $=$ .0033mm because *we know* that each division of the stage micrometer equals .01mm. Therefore, each division of the disc equals 3.3 microns. If we now remove the stage micrometer from the microscope and measure a specimen which takes in ten divisions of the disc, we know that the true length of the specimen is .033mm or 33 microns.

We do the same thing when we calibrate a screw micrometer eyepiece, and with it we have the additional advantage of being able to estimate very closely one hundredth part of the calibration constant because the drum is divided into 100 parts. Exactly the same is true of the filar micrometer.

If a stage micrometer divided in .001 of an inch is used the procedure and results would be identical except that our answer would be in thousandths of an inch instead of in parts of a millimeter.

We must also remember that if the tube length of a microscope is changed the calibration constant of the disc also changes. Likewise, if a binocular microscope is used, the same interpupillary setting employed when making the calibration must also be used when measuring an object because the calibration constant changes a little with a different interpupillary distance. The only exception to this in binocular microscopes is that type so constructed that the tube length does not change at all for different interpupillary distances. *Always use exactly the same tube length for calibration and measurements.*

The following table may be of help to persons who must compare values in parts of an inch with parts of a millimeter. The comparisons are not absolutely exact, but they are close enough for most practical purposes.

.000001 of an inch	equals	.025 microns *	
.00001 " " "	"	.25 "	**
.000039 " " "	"	1.0 "	
.0001 " " "	"	2.5 "	
.001 " " "	"	25.0 "	
.01 " " "	"	254.0 "	
.1 " " "	"	2540.0 "	
1.0 " " "	"	25400.0 "	

* Cannot be seen by the human eye.
** Near the limit of resolution of the human eye.

Proper Magnification for Measurements

The question is often asked: What magnification should I use to measure to a tolerance of x inches or millimeters? This is easily determined by keeping in mind the theory of magnification (See "Magnification" in Glossary). We must magnify an object so that when viewed in a microscope it appears sufficiently large to the eye so that it can be easily measured with a regular millimeter ruler. Now then, we certainly can measure 1 mm with the unaided eye, therefore an object which we think is 1 micron long needs a magnification of 1,000 times before we can measure it properly. An object so magnified would look in the microscope as if it were 1mm long and could then be measured. If we magnified it 2,000 times we could measure it still easier because it would look like 2mm. If we only magnified it 500 times the measurement would be difficult because it would look like half of a millimeter.

The following general rule may be helpful:

For objects of 25 to 30 microns magnification needed is about 100 times.

For objects of 2.5 to 5 microns magnification needed is about 400 to 500 times.

For objects of 1 to 2 microns magnification needed is about 600 to 1,000 times.

For smaller objects or tolerances magnification needed is about 1,200 to 2,000 times.

If convenient and practical use for measurements a magnification which is slightly greater than the minimums suggested above. *In measurements, some "empty magnification" is sometimes quite useful.*

Counting Chambers

These chambers are built with great precision and used considerably for various purposes. They are designed to count, on the volume basis, particles in suspension in some liquid.

They are heavy glass slides in which a cell has been ground. The cell has an exact depth so that when covered with *an optically flat* cover glass the volume of the cell per unit area is accurately known. On the floor of the cell fine lines are drawn in convenient patterns so that the particles are seen over the ruled squares, etc., and the count made on the volume basis.

Courtesy Spencer Lens Co.

FIGURE 104

Haemacytometer Counting Chamber.

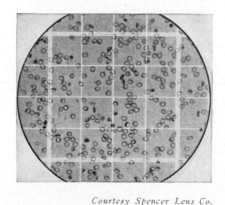

Courtesy Spencer Lens Co.

FIGURE 104A

Photomicrograph of blood cells on a counting chamber.

The most general use of these counting chambers is in counting red and white blood cells. Standard techniques have been developed for this purpose. Usually the drop of blood is drawn and diluted in a blood pipette according to the standard techniques, then after covering the cell with the cover glass the liquid is released by the side of the cover glass and capillary attraction fills the cell so that an accurate count of the blood cells can be made. Some of these chambers have the lines of the ruling cut through a semi-opaque metallic surface which has been deposited on the glass. The result therefore is white lines on a semi-dark field which makes it possible to see the lines much better.*

Counting chambers are also used for some spinal fluid and bacteriological work. There is also the Howard Mold Counting Chamber previously mentioned which is also designed for the volume method of counting. Its construction however is somewhat different from that described above as the floor of the cell is not ruled. The micrometer disc designed to go with it takes the place of the usual counting chamber rulings.

Eyepiece Holders for Monocular Microscopes

The *inclined monocular eyepiece holder* is a very convenient accessory. It fits in the tube of the microscope in place of the regular eyepiece holder. A prism

Courtesy Bausch & Lomb Opt. Co.

FIGURE 105

Inclined monocular eyepiece holder.

* Spencer Bright Line Chambers.

changes the direction of the light so that the eyepiece is held in an inclined position. This permits the worker to sit at his microscope in an upright natural position without the necessity of inclining the microscope, a valuable feature when observing specimens in liquids.

Binocular Eyepiece Holders are made with vertical and inclined tubes. They also fit in the tube of the microscope in place of the regular eyepiece holder. Generally the type with the vertical tubes is not very practical because the eyepieces are up so high that the worker is uncomfortable unless he inclines his microscope through a considerable arc. *These holders should not be confused with the standard binocular bodies of the regular binocular microscopes which fit directly over the nosepiece and are therefore perfectly comfortable.*

The inclined type of binocular eyepiece holder is perfectly practical and gives good results.

Since the tube length is longer when these binocular holders are used, the magnification obtained is much greater than the rated magnification of a given optical system. This is not objectionable if this additional tube length is compensated for optically by means of compensating lenses in the holder.

Polarizing Accessories *

Any standard microscope can be equipped for *limited* observations with polarized light by purchasing the necessary polarizing accessories.

They consist of (a), a polarizer which takes the place of the condenser, and (b), an analyzer so mounted that it can be placed over, and rotated around, the eyepiece

* Also see Chapter VIII Polarizing Microscopes.

of the microscope. Usually these "cap analyzers" are graduated to 5 degrees of rotation. In every combination of analyzer and polarizer it is desirable that at least one of the elements be graduated. The "Nicol" prism is generally used in these polarizers and the Glan-Thompson prism in the analyzer.

There are also analyzers so mounted that they can be attached to the lower end of the tube of the microscope. They are threaded to receive the objectives. Such analyzers are used instead of the "cap" type. Generally they are rotatable but ungraduated.

These accessories are useful for merely recognizing

Courtesy Spencer Lens

FIGURE 106

Analyzer and Polarizer.

anisotropic material. For the determination of extinction angles and other optical characteristics, the microscope must have a graduated revolving stage and a cross hair eyepiece as well as strain free objectives.

Since the advent of "Polaroid" it is possible to secure some very helpful polarizing accessories made with this material. They serve as very good inexpensive substitutes for polarizing prisms in some kinds of work. There is the "cap polarizer" designed for use with microscopes without substage fittings (the usual high school instruments). It rests on the substage diaphragm slightly below the stage surface level. For microscopes with condensers there is the disc polarizer which fits beneath the iris diaphragm of the condenser. The analyzer is also a polaroid disc so mounted that it fits over any standard eyepiece. With a combination of analyzer and polarizer discs it is possible to determine whether a material is isotropic or anisotropic and to view the beautiful colors of polarization.

Courtesy Bausch & Lomb Opt. Co.

| First Order Red | Quarter Wave | Cap | Disc | Cap |
| Retardation Plate | Retardation Plate | Analyzer | Polarizer | Polarizer |

FIGURE 107

"Polaroid" accessories.

The addition to the equipment of retardation plates extends the range and variety of work possible with these accessories. These plates are mounted so that they fit inside the mount of the cap analyzer. The red of the first order plate is used to detect weak double refraction, to estimate the order of interference color in Newton's scale and to determine the fast and slow axes of the specimen. It also provides some very vivid color effects when used with certain specimens. The quarter wave retardation plate is used to determine whether a crystal is positive or negative by observing the interference figure at the back of the objective. For this determination it is necessary to remove first the eyepiece of the microscope. This quarter wave plate is also used to determine whether optically active substances are dextrorotatory or laevorotatory.

Mechanical Stages

Since the magnification of a microscope increases both size and movement, it is highly desirable to be able to move the specimen *with some mechanical device*. Complete control over the movement of the object is essential with high magnifications (400X up). When an object is moved while magnified let us say 1000 times, it appears to move 1000 times farther and faster than it really does move. The difficulty of keeping such an object in view while it moves across the field with the speed of an express train is obvious. This is the reason for the development of mechanical stages which, because of their convenience are now in almost universal use. Furthermore those mechanical stages which are graduated are also very helpful to relocate

Courtesy Spencer Lens Co.

FIGURE 108

Research built on mechanical stages.

an object in the field of the microscope by noting its previous location shown by the verniers.*

Measuring an object with a mechanical stage: A graduated mechanical stage can be used for measurements of objects which are not too small (100 or more microns). A good method is to use a cross hair disc

* See "How to Read a Vernier," Chapter V.

in the eyepiece and to move the object until one side of it touches the hair line, the reading on the mechanical stage is noted and the object moved until its other side reaches the cross hair. The new reading is also noted and the difference between the two readings is the length of the object. Since mechanical stages are usually graduated in millimeters, and their verniers to tenths of a millimeter, it is possible to measure to 100 microns which equals 0.1 mm.

Types of mechanical stages: These accessories are made in many different types. There are those microscope stages which have their mechanical movement as an integral part of their construction, fig. 108. Some are rectangular and others circular. The latter type is also shown in the illustrations of the research micro-

FIGURE 109
Ungraduated attachable mechanical stage.

scopes, figs. 70 and 72. These mechanical stages actually are not true accessories because they cannot be added to the stage of a microscope, but in some cases the "plane" stage of a microscope can be *replaced* with one of this type. Their movement is very exact and easily controlled.

For mechanical movement only, we have the un-graduated mechanical stages. These are very popular because they perform well the main purpose of this accessory, the controlled movement of the object. They are comparatively inexpensive and can be added to any microscope which has a rectangular stage.

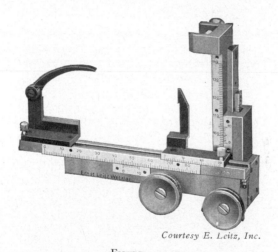

Courtesy E. Leitz, Inc.

FIGURE 110

Graduated attachable mechanical stage.

There are also the attachable graduated mechanical stages similar to the previous type but with graduations. They are also made in some models which permit their adaptation to a plain circular revolving stage. The latter are often used with polarizing microscopes.

FIGURE 111

Attachable graduated mechanical stage for circular revolving stage.

The Camera Lucida

This is a very useful accessory for making drawings of microscopic objects under observation. By referring to fig. 112 we see that it is attached to the top of the tube of the microscope. It consists of a small prism which lies over the eyepiece. Around this prism is a rotatable mount having several neutral tint filters of different light transmitting properties. Also below the prism is another set of neutral tint filters any one of which can be rotated into position. These filters balance the light coming to the eye from the mirror and from the eyepiece. A bar extends to the side and supports the mirror which can be inclined to the proper angle. The drawing paper is placed under the mirror and can be seen simultaneously with the object under observation. This means that if a pencil is held over the paper we can see it and its movement as if it were under the lens of the microscope. Very accurate drawings can be made in this manner. Usually the outline and main parts of the object are carefully drawn with the Camera

FIGURE 112

Camera Lucida.

Lucida and then the minute details are filled in free hand. The trick is to balance the light from the paper with that from the microscope so that neither will be greater than the other. This is done mainly with the filters but a change one way or the other of the illumination of the paper is helpful at times. With a little practice it is possible to obtain the ideal balance of light necessary for good drawings.

Some Camera Lucidas are made without the filters

below the prism, in other words, only with the filters which go between the prism and the mirror. Also, some camera lucidas do not have the centering screws necessary to center the prism very carefully over the eyepiece. There are also other simpler types which do not have extendable arms and movable mirrors, etc. The cost of these accessories varies in proportion to their completeness and workmanship.

Demonstration Oculars

These oculars can be used on any microscope to allow two persons to view the same field at the same time. They are of inestimable value in educational institutions both for teaching and quizzes. A movable pointer, which can also be seen in the field, makes possible the locating of a given point of the object.

The two most popular types are illustrated in figs. 113 and 114. One has the side tube inclined and the

Courtesy Bausch & Lomb Opt. Co.

FIGURE 113

Demonstration Ocular with inclined tube.

other horizontal. The latter is more expensive because an additional prism is required in its construction. In the first, one person looks down into the microscope and the other person sideways into the ocular at the

Courtesy Spencer Lens Co.

FIGURE 114

Demonstration Ocular with horizontal tube.

side tube. In the second, both people look down into the oculars. The visual results are identical with both types. They both have means of focusing the eyepiece in the side tube to neutralize any difference in the eyes of any two persons.

Comparison Eyepieces

This is the type of eyepiece used with the Bullet Comparison Microscopes.* They are also used to connect any two microscopes and examine two different specimens side by side. Where considerable comparison work is necessary they are invaluable for the only alternative is to take two photomicrographs of the ob-

* Chapter VII.

jects under *exactly* the same conditions and then compare the results. These eyepieces combine the two
images into a single eye lens, one half of the field showing one object and the other half the other.

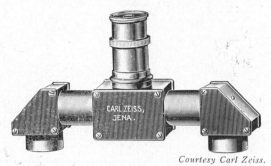

Courtesy Carl Zeiss.

FIGURE 115
Comparison Eyepiece.

When doing this type of work it is better to have
the objectives and eyepieces of the microscopes well
matched for magnification, size of field, etc. The two
microscopes should be focused at the same time very
carefully keeping the comparison eyepiece always in a
horizontal position.

Photomicrographic Cameras and Their Use

This is a very extensive subject which actually requires a complete volume for its proper discussion. In
the bibliography one such reference book is listed which
has 352 pages. Obviously therefore, here we can only
give the reader a very elementary idea of this subject
which may serve as a guide for further investigation.

At times it is desirable, and very often essential, to
make a permanent record of microscopic observations
for future reference. We have seen in the previous
pages that this can be done by "projection drawing"

(Chapter V) and with the aid of the Camera Lucida (Chapter IX). However, the use of the photomicrographic camera is much more rapid and much less laborious. Furthermore, since the advent of colored photography and films such as "Kodachrome" it is possible to photograph microscopic objects in their natural colors. A suggested technique for the taking of color photomicrographs will be found later on in this chapter.

Photomicrography is not to be confused with *photomacrography*. The first requires the combined use of a camera and the microscope. The second does not require a microscope but rather the use directly on the camera of special photographic lenses of limited magnifying power. Photomacrographs are usually 15 diameters or less.

There are many types of photomicrographic cameras in the market. They vary in price from the very inexpensive to the very complete equipments which are quite costly. Generally it is always better to use a specially designed camera for this work, but with patience, and skill developed with practice, it is possible to obtain good results with the less expensive cameras.

Types of Cameras: Basically we can divide these instruments into the following types:

1. Those which are attached directly to the tube of the microscope. In this classification are found also the miniature cameras with their necessary accessories for photomicrography (Leica, etc., ideal for Kodachrome work).

2. Those which are supported by a stand of some kind independent of the microscope itself. These in turn are divided into:

FIGURE 116

Photomicrographic Camera attachable to any microscope.

a. Cameras *without bellows* which are limited to the magnification used in the microscope and which reproduce the object near same magnification ten inches away from the eyepoint of the eyepiece of the microscope. These cameras usually have a side viewing eyepiece (fig. 117). The plate is 10 inches away from the microscope eyepiece.

b. Cameras *with bellows* by means of which it is possible to place the plate less than 10 inches away from the eyepiece, which gives a lower magnification than we would obtain at 10 inches. The plate can also be placed away from the eyepiece farther than 10 inches which gives us correspondingly higher magnifications. In this camera the focusing is done by watching the ground glass on the top of the camera, then removing it and inserting the plate or cut film in its place.

Both A and B have their advantages and disadvantages: A, is generally easier to use and more photomicrographs can be taken within a specified time. On the other hand, B has the tremendous advantage of variable magnification with the same set of objective and eyepiece of the microscope. At times this is *very desirable*.

For routine work A is probably more practical, for research B would be better.

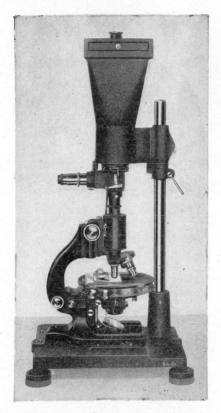

FIGURE 117

Photomicrographic Camera with side focusing eyepiece and stand.

3. Finally, there are the large cameras on horizontal optical benches which permit very great enlargements due to their long bellows. They are most generally

Courtesy Bausch & Lomb Opt. Co.

FIGURE 118

Photomicrographic Camera with bellows.

used with the large metallographic equipments and in completely equipped photomicrographic laboratories. Powerful illumination is necessary for their proper use.

Photomicrographic cameras generally do not have lenses. Actually they are only dark chambers with a shutter at one end and the photographic plate at the other. The lens system of the microscope forms the desired image and projects it to the plate for recording. If a camera equipped with a lens of its own is used, it is necessary to set the lens at infinity unless some other provision has been made by the manufacturer for photomicrographic work.

As we said before, with the cameras listed as 2A, the magnification obtained is near same as that rendered by the optical system of the microscope. If we want to change the magnification, we must change the lenses of the microscope itself.

If we want to establish the magnification obtained with a camera equipped with extendable bellows (2B or 3) at a given bellow extension, we use a stage micrometer slide as our object and project its image to the ground glass of the camera. We then establish the magnification in exactly the same way described under Drawings and Measurements by Projection (Chapter V). The only difference is that the magnified image of the stage micrometer is on the ground glass instead of on a piece of paper.

The use of Photomicrographic Cameras varies considerably according to their construction, but there are a few general rules which must be followed to obtain good pictures.

The microscope is placed under the camera, centered and focused to the ground glass or the focusing telescope. *Photographic eyepieces* are used to correct the residual curvature of field of the objective and to avoid distortion. Köhler illumination is preferable. The diaphragm of the lamp (field stop) must be closed to the area of the field photographed. Otherwise the glare will prevent a photograph of good definition. Apochromatic objectives, compensating eyepieces, and a corrected condenser are necessary for the best rendering of colored objects, especially if separation negatives are made directly from the microscope.

The condenser of the microscope must be properly focused, as is done with the Köhler method, when natural color photomicrographs are taken, otherwise the background may be tinted from the chromatic aberrations of the condenser and the colors of the specimen may be affected.

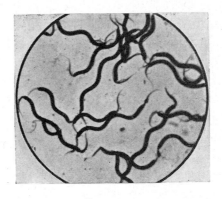

FIGURE 119
Giant Spirillum 400X.

The exposure may be determined by making a trial negative with a series of different exposures. This can be done in the following manner. We make the first exposure let us say at 2 seconds, and we then insert under the plate the plate holder slider about ¼ of the way across the plate. Thus we know that exposure number 1 is 2 seconds. We make the second exposure at say 3 seconds and push in the slider another quarter of the way. Our second exposure then is 2 + 3 or 5 seconds. The third exposure is made at 4 seconds and we have exposure number 3 at 2 + 3 + 4 or 9 seconds. After pushing in the slider another quarter of the way we take our fourth and last exposure at say 6 seconds, which would make it a 15 second exposure. The result would then be a negative having four different exposures of the same object taken under identical conditions. We can then decide whether to take our final picture at 2, 5, 9, or 15 seconds and we can be pretty sure of what the results will be without wasting several plates.

An approximate exposure may be obtained also from an exposure meter. Move the object to one side so that only clear glass shows in the field. Place a photoelectric exposure meter at the level of the plate (after removing the ground glass). The exposure is read from the meter set to the emulsion speed used at the f 2 position on the meter. This is an arbitrary value that gives good results for the average microscope slide. Very dense or very transparent specimens may take somewhat longer or shorter exposures.

The magnification must be sufficient to make the detail resolved by the microscope large enough to be within the resolving power of the plate or film and to be seen. Enlargement of the negative or projection of the positive must be considered when that type of examination is to be used. Fast panchromatic emulsions resolve 40 to 60 lines per millimeter, positive emulsions around 100 and slow contrast emulsions about 175 lines per millimeter. A strict standard of definition for contact prints to be examined without further enlargements is 300 times the N.A. of the objective used. If a lower

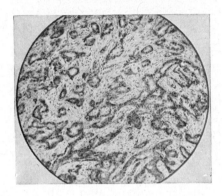

FIGURE 120

Adeno carcinoma of the breast 45X.

standard of definition is acceptable, the magnification may be increased to 1000 N.A. and even more. With ultraviolet radiation, greater magnification may be useful.

The use of colored filters is very valuable. Every photomicrographer should have a set of Wratten * filters, unless he is making only natural color pictures in which case the technique is different. Contrast can be accentuated with their use. A red object can be made to stand out better by using a green filter between the lamp and the mirror of the microscope. Conversely, a green object is accentuated by a red filter. It is also possible to bring out detail and suppress contrast by using a filter of the nearest possible color to that of the specimen. Another possibility is to choose a filter of

* Set consists of 9 filters—sold by Eastman Kodak Co.

a complementary color to that of the specimen in order to improve contrast on certain light colored objects. For example a slight yellow color can be made to stand out on a black and white picture by using a deep blue filter, etc.

Since until now the use of Kodachrome is comparatively new in photomicrography, the techniques are not as well developed and established for this work. Many workers take several pictures at different exposures on the "indoors film" (without a blue filter on the lamp), and then choose the best one. No doubt in time more precise techniques will be developed.

The following method * for determining the correct exposure, other than that of trial and error, works quite well for both black and white and Kodachrome. First we must measure the diameter of the Ramsden Circle given by our optical train. The Ramsden Circle can be measured with a stage micrometer and a magnifier by holding over the eyepiece (quite close to it) a piece

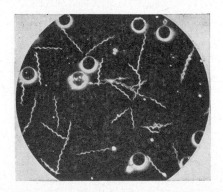

FIGURE 121

Spirochaeta obermeyerii (dark field illumination) 630X.

* Suggested by Mr. Paul Rittenhouse of the N. Y. Microscopical Society.

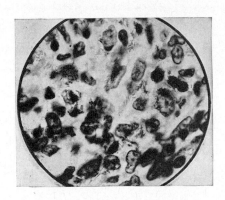

FIGURE 122

Microbacterium leprae 300X.

of ground glass with the ground side up and finding the position at which the disc is in perfect focus. The stage micrometer is placed over the ground glass image of the circle with the graduation down and with a hand lens of 4 to 6X the diameter of the Ramsden Circle can be measured.

Multiply *half* of the diameter of the Ramsden Circle (in millimeters) by the magnification of the ocular and then divide the result by the focal length of the objective in use (in millimeters). The result will be a close approximation to the N.A. of the complete optical system used. Then divide .5 by this N.A. value and we obtain the F factor. If we then place our exposure meter at the plane where the plate or film will be (without any ground glass between the meter and the light), we can read the exposure from the meter set to the emulsion speed used at the F position which we have just established. The object which we are going to photograph is in place on the microscope while we are establishing both the N.A. and the F values as well as when we take our meter reading.

With a meter as sensitive as the Weston Master No. 715, direct readings can be taken with most subjects illuminated by substage condenser with plain or polarized light, and with the photographic plate or film as much as two inches from the eye point, using objectives up to 16 millimeters.

Where the brightness is not sufficient at the emulsion plane, for direct reading, some form of relative factor basis must be used. For example, suppose we get a meter reading with the meter one inch from the ocular but wish a larger magnification, with the film or plate at 4 inches. Take the reading with the light-sensitive cell of the meter at 1 inch and multiply the exposure so obtained, by 16 (since illumination follows a square law in relation to distance).

Again, suppose we are using polarized light with an object that is dull when the polarizing prisms are crossed (maximum extinction). In this case some form of filter-wedge exposure meter such as the Heyden Aktino Photo Meter can be used to establish a relative factor basis directly. For example, we may secure sufficient brilliance for a meter reading, with the upper prism (analyzer) rotated off the extinction angle. Having established the exposure here, we use the wedge-filter meter to find the *ratio* of exposure between this position of the analyzer and with maximum extinction. Then multiply the exposure time just found by the *ratio* of exposure found with the filter-wedge meter.

Lacking such a filter-wedge meter, we can use fifty or sixty 1-inch discs cut from a *single* sheet of cellophane (of blue-green color, for accuracy). With the improvised cellophane-disc method, we establish the *ratio* of exposure by adding discs until the detail of the object can just be discerned when illuminated for the photograph, and add discs until we have the same visual effect with the higher illumination gauged with the electronic meter: then the ratio of the two quantities of discs is the exposure *ratio*.

This *ratio* method will not of course be valid if any of the factors used for obtaining the N.A. value are changed.

In conclusion we must state that only with practice and experience is it possible to develop adequate skill in obtaining consistently good photomicrographs.

Chapter X

COMMON ERRORS IN THE USE OF THE MICROSCOPE

As we have seen in the previous chapters, in order to obtain the best results of which a microscope is capable, it is necessary to use it properly. Only in this way can we profit from the various possible adjustments and the perfection of its optics and general workmanship.

We have also seen that any careful individual can learn to use it properly, and with practice he can eventually become really proficient in its use. Nevertheless there are many students, technicians and even scientists who, although they use the microscope to considerable advantage, do not get from its use optimum results. This is the reason why at times they find it difficult to really *see* some details that they know, or at least suspect, should be there. If a person has some knowledge of the optical principles of the microscope outlined in the previous pages, and of the proper technique when making his observations, he should not encounter any serious difficulties when working with his microscope.

Students especially should learn at the beginning the proper technique so that they will not grow careless and get in the habit of making errors which will affect adversely the results of their microscopic observations.

We submit the following list of common errors as a *red flag* which means DANGER. If these errors are carefully guarded against the microscopist is very much more likely to obtain good results with his microscope be it "simple" or "compound."

In the Use of "Simple" Microscopes

1. It is impossible to get good results with a magnifier of 6X or more unless the eye is placed very near to the lens. This is true whether the lens is used as a "hand lens" or mounted on a small dissecting microscope stand. The eye should be 4 or 5mm away from the lens. If this is not done, the field of view will be materially reduced and the magnification will not be that for which the lens is rated.

2. Do not use a lens of more than 15X with a dissecting microscope of the "simple" type. If the lens has a greater magnification it is usually very difficult to avoid error #1. The best lenses to use in order of their convenience are 6X, 9 or 10X, 12X and 15X.

3. Do not attempt to use a lens unless it is clean. Watch for fingerprints on the lens surfaces as they cloud the image.

In the Use of Compound Microscopes

1. Do not use the concave surface of your microscope mirror if the instrument is equipped with a condenser. The only exceptions to this are (a), that mentioned under "mirror" at the beginning of Chapter II (which is only the lesser of two evils) and, (b), when

objectives of a magnification of less than 10X are used. In the latter case the error is not serious but it is there just the same.

2. Do not close the iris diaphragm of your microscope condenser to a point where the "balance" of the optical system is affected. If you close it so much that the cone of light it delivers has a lesser optical angle than that of the objective used, the N.A. value of the objective will be lowered. This is not important if it is only necessary to bring out contrast in the specimen, but it is important if fine detail is under observation. It is also just as bad to open the iris of the condenser beyond the N.A. of the objective for this gives glare. Always balance your optical system.

3. If it is desirable to reach the maximum N.A. of an oil immersion objective, it is absolutely necessary to have an oil contact, free of air bubbles, between the top lens of the condenser and the lower surface of the slide. If this is not done, the highest possible N.A. is about 1.00 regardless of the rated N.A. of the objective used. The oil contact between the front lens of the objective and the slide should also be free of air bubbles.

4. Never put oil or water *inside* an immersion objective or any kind of objective. *This will ruin it.**

5. It is impossible to obtain optimum results from a highly corrected condenser (achromatic) unless it is carefully centered and focused.

6. Always use an apochromatic objective with compensating oculars or their equivalent. Their best results are not possible if ordinary huyghenian oculars are used with these objectives.

* This may read rather extreme but is not. It is surprising how many students actually do this if they have not been properly instructed in the use of immersion lenses.

7. It is best to match the make of a set of apochromatic objectives and compensating oculars. Use a Spencer apochromatic objective with a Spencer compensating ocular, a Zeiss with a Zeiss, etc. This is not always necessary with achromatic and fluorite objectives.

8. Never immerse an objective in the oil while looking in the ocular. While immersion is being made always look from the side until it is accomplished, then focus with the *Fine Adjustment*.

9. Always be sure to adjust for your eyes the interpupillary distance of the tubes of a binocular microscope. Good and comfortable results are not possible otherwise.

10. When using a binocular microscope *both* eyes should be in perfect focus. Most binocular microscopes have an independent adjustment in one of the tubes to accomplish this. The fine adjustment of the microscope is used to focus one eye, and the tube adjustment is then used to focus the other eye. When this is properly done both eyes are in perfect focus.

11. Be sure to remember that a binocular microscope requires more light than a monocular. It is impossible to get good results if insufficient light is used.

12. Many people cannot use to advantage the formula of 1000 times the N.A. of the objective which should be applied to avoid "empty magnification." If this is so in your case use the 750 times or the 500 times formula.

13. Never use immersion oil to lubricate a microscope, microtome or bearing. It gets gummy and eventually solidifies. Use regular lubricants like vaseline or pike oil. If vaseline is used it is better to mix it with a little lanoline.

14. Never use a microscope until you are sure that

its entire optical system is perfectly clean. Watch out for finger prints on the front lens of the objectives and on both lens surfaces of the eyepieces.

15. Do not attempt to use a dark field condenser unless there is oil contact, free of air bubbles, between the top lens and the lower surface of the slide. *Remember the funnel stop if an oil immersion objective is used*.

16. If a high N.A. objective is used, be sure that the N.A. of the condenser matches it. If an objective of N.A. 1.40 is used with a condenser of N.A. 1.25 the highest N.A. possible with the objective is about 1.25.

17. It is difficult to examine properly under high magnifications a thick specimen if transmitted light is used. For high power examinations the sections should be no more than 8 microns thick, if possible 4 or 6.

18. If xylene is used to clean an objective, use only very little of it and then dry it immediately with a clean soft cloth or lens paper.

19. It is wasteful and messy to use more immersion oil on a slide than absolutely necessary to obtain a good immersion contact with the front lens of an oil immersion lens. Don't smear oil all over the slide.

20. Standard high dry objectives should always be used with a cover glass of the correct thickness. If they are used without a cover glass the image will appear cloudy. If the objective used is an apochromat use the correction collar for best results.

21. Always make sure that the slide is placed on the microscope right side up. If it is upside down, there is danger of damaging another objective as it is swung into position when changing from one to the other. Also, error number 20 occurs immediately and an oil immersion lens cannot be brought down near enough to the specimen to be focused.

22. Never change the paired objectives from one *stereoscopic* microscope to another, or in the same microscope, from one position in the nosepiece to another. The objectives are centered at the factory to each specific binocular body and at a predetermined position in the nosepiece.

23. A polarizing microscope usually requires approximately the same light intensity as a binocular microscope. This is due to the great loss of light which takes place when ordinary light is polarized by the prisms. Don't attempt to use these microscopes for high magnifications with little substage lamps.

24. The centering of the objectives is essential on a polarizing microscope. Always check this before beginning to work with such an instrument.

25. It is impossible to obtain accurate results with a polarizing microscope unless its objectives are "free of strain."

26. For best results with a metallurgical microscope always use "short mount objectives."

27. If the graduations of a micrometer disc cannot be seen clearly the chances are that it was placed in the ocular upside down. If this is not the case and still they are not distinct, then the diaphragm of the ocular is in the wrong position for your eyes.

28. Always focus carefully the eye lens of a micrometer eyepiece, screw micrometer, filar micrometer and cross hair oculars of the polarizing microscopes. The dividing lines should be in perfect focus before observations begin.

29. In making visual measurements with a microscope use the same tube length which was used to calibrate the micrometer disc. If a binocular microscope

is used the same is true for the interpupillary distance (with most microscopes).

30. If the results obtained with a camera lucida are not good this is probably due to the fact that the light coming through the microscope is not properly balanced with that coming from the paper.

31. When projecting with a microscope the focus of the condenser is very important. If it is not properly focused there may be color fringes on the image.

32. Most cameras equipped with lenses of their own require the positioning of the lens at "infinity" when they are used to take photomicrographs.

33. If photomicrographs are poor watch for extraneous reflections of light and make a trial negative at various time exposures. Follow manufacturer's instructions for the operation of the camera. Many people do not read important instructions before attempting to work with an unfamiliar instrument.

34. Remember that *too much* light is just as bad an error as *not enough light*. This is true in the simple microscopes as well as in the compound instruments. Also watch for outside light and reflections falling on the eyepieces or on the top lens of a simple magnifier.

Table of Magnifications of Old Objectives and Eyepieces Marked with Old Designations

Since there are still in use many old objectives and eyepieces, it is possible that the following tables will be of help to those who do not know the magnification and other factors covered by such old designations. The old markings of microscope optics did not show their magnification, they were simply engraved with a number, such as, 1, 2, 3 etc. for the objectives and I, II, III etc. for the eyepieces.—See page 286.

Courtesy of E. Leitz, Inc.

HUYGENS EYEPIECES—Optical Data

Magn. No.	Equivalent Focal Length mm	Old Designation No.	Magn. No.	Equivalent Focal Length mm	Old Designation No.
4X	62.5	O	10X	25.0	IV
5X	50.0	I	12X	20.85	V
6X	41.65	II	16X	15.62	VI
8X	31.25	III			

ACHROMATIC OBJECTIVES—Optical Data

Magn. No.	Equivalent Focal Length mm	Type of Objective	Old Designation No.	N.A.	Working Distance mm	Micrometer Value[†] with Eyepiece 6X mm
1X	56	Dry	0	0.05	55	0.143
2.7X	42	Dry	1	0.08	40	0.058
3.2X	24	Dry	1K	0.08	3.2	0.0445
3.2X	40	Dry	1	0.12	34.5	0.049
4.3X	32	Dry	1b	0.15	27	0.037
6X	24	Dry	2	0.20	16	0.0275
8X	20	Dry	2b	0.30	7.7	0.02
10X	16	Dry	3R	0.25	5.8	0.0156
14X	13	Dry	3b	0.40	3.2	0.012
22X	9	Dry	4	0.45	2.0	0.0075
24X	8	Dry	4	0.50	0.8	0.0065
30X	6	Dry	5	0.65	0.75	0.005
45X	4	Dry	6	0.85	0.32	0.0036
45X	4	Dry	6L	0.65	0.60	0.0036
62X	3	Dry	7	0.85	0.28	0.0025
50X	3.6	Water Im.	1/7W	1.00	0.40	0.003
90X	2.1	Water Im.	10	1.20	0.10	0.0018
10X	16	Oil Im.	.16mm	0.25	0.65	0.016
22X	8	Oil Im.	8mm	0.65	0.45	0.008
100X	1.8	Oil Im.	1/12	1.30	0.11	0.0016
90X	1.8	Oil Im.	1/12	1.25	0.15	0.00175

† Value on the stage of 0.1mm in the focal plane of the eyepiece.

FLUORITE (SEMI-APOCHROMATIC) OBJECTIVES—Optical Data

Magn. No.	Equivalent Focal Length mm	Type of Objective	Old Designation No.	N.A.	Working Distance mm	Micrometer Value[‡] with Eyepiece 6X mm
42X	4.2	Dry	6a	0.85	0.38	0.0038
58X	3.2	Dry	7a	0.85	0.28	0.0028
70X	2.6	Dry	8a	0.90	0.25	0.0023
85X	2.2	Dry	9a	0.90	0.13	0.0018
54X	3.45	Oil Im.	1/7a	0.95	0.20	0.003
70X	2.6	Oil Im.	1/10a	1.30	0.18	0.0022
95X	1.95	Oil Im.	1/12a	1.32	0.11	0.0017
114X	1.6	Oil Im.	1/16a	1.32	0.08	0.0014

‡ Value on the stage of 0.1mm in the focal plane of the eyepiece.

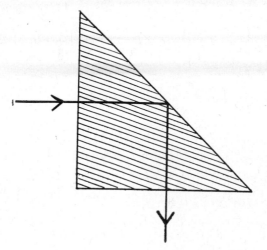

1. *Prism* showing path of light.

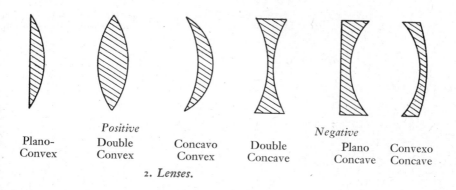

Positive

Plano-
Convex
Double
Convex
Concavo
Convex
Double
Concave
Plano
Concave
Convexo
Concave

Negative

2. *Lenses.*

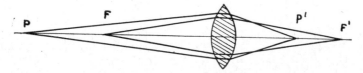

P   F   P′   F′

Focus and Focal Distance—When F is moved to P,
then F′ moves to P′ or vice versa.

287

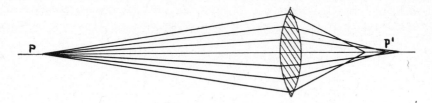

Spherical Aberration—Notice how the rays coming through the margin of the lens bend more than those near the center.

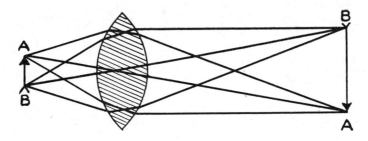

Image Formation—Note how the arrow (the image) has been turned upside down after the rays have passed through the lens and formed an image.

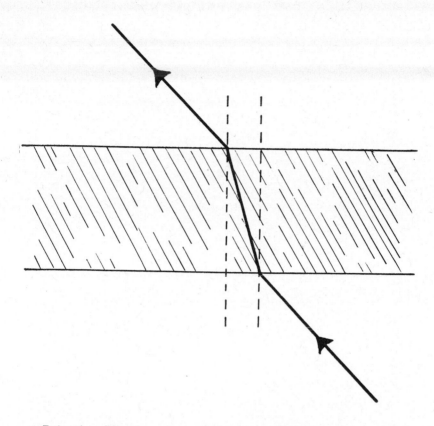

Refraction—Note how the ray is bent *toward* the perpendicular as it enters at an angle from air to glass (from a medium of less density to one of greater density) and when it emerges it is bent *away from* the perpendicular (from a dense medium to one *less* dense).

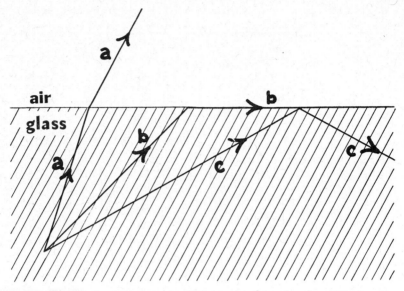

Critical Angle—Note how ray "A" emerges from the glass, "B" emerges but continues parallel to the surface and "C" reaches the surface of the glass at such an oblique angle that it cannot emerge and is reflected back into the glass. See Glossary "Critical Angle."

GLOSSARY

The following words and terms are used in relation to the microscope. All of them have not been used in the text. However this glossary is valuable not only for quick clarification of terms but also may serve of itself as a reference and *source of additional practical information* on the microscope and its accessories. The definitions offered are not strictly technical. They are intended to fill the need for rapid practical reference rather than full scientific clarification.

A

Abbe, Ernst
Famous German physicist, 1845–1905. Originator of the Abbe condenser. Made many important contributions in the field of optics.

Abbe Apertometer
See Apertometer.

Abbe Condenser
See Condenser.

Abbe Test Plate
See Test Plate.

Aberration, Chromatic
A defect of lenses relating to color. Caused by light of different wave lengths coming to a focus at different points. The result of such defect is to distort color values.

Aberration, Spherical
A defect in lenses which have a spherically ground surface. This is due to the fact that the rays passing through the lens near the margin bend at a greater angle than those which pass

near the center of the lens. This defect tends to distort lines and shapes.

Achromatic

The absence of chromatic aberration. These lenses are corrected so as to transmit an approximation to true color values through the optical system. This is done by bringing two colors of the spectrum to the same focus and the others neutralized as much as possible.

Adjustment, Coarse

The adjustment by which a microscope is approximately focused. It usually consists of a rack and pinion and makes it possible to move the tube noticeable distances with few turns of the pinion.

Adjustment, Fine

The adjustment by which a microscope is accurately focused. It usually consists of a micrometer screw movement or a similar device. This movement is usually limited to about 2mm.

Analyzer

The polarizing device (prism or otherwise) which is placed above the objective to repolarize the light coming from the substage of a microscope. (See also Polarizer.)

Anastigmatic

The correction of astigmatism. Usually accomplished by cylindrical lenses.

Angle of Incidence

The angle made by an incident ray with the perpendicular to the surface which reflects it.

Angle of Refraction

The angle which an emergent ray makes with the perpendicular to the surface from which it emerges.

Angular Aperture

The angle of a cone of light which can enter the front lens of an objective from the axial point of the object plane.

Apertometer

An instrument for measuring the angular aperture of an objective.

Aplanatic

Corrected for spherical aberration so that the marginal rays as well as the central rays come to a focus at the same point.

Apochromatic

A better correction than the achromatic. In a lens this means that three colors of the spectrum have been brought to the same focus and that it has been corrected for spherical aberration for two colors.

Arm, of a Microscope
The part of a microscope which supports the tube.

Aspheric
Does not have the shape of a sphere. An aspheric lens cannot have a spherical surface.

Astigmatism
A condition of unequal curvatures along the different meridians in one or more refractive surfaces in consequence of which the rays from a luminous point are not focused at a single point, but are spread out as a line in one or another direction.

Axis, pl. axes, Crystallographic
See Crystallographic Axis.

Axis, Optic
See Optic Axis.

B

Babinet Compensator
See Compensator

Base, of a Microscope
The foot of the microscope which is usually shaped like a horseshoe.

Berek Compensator
See Compensator.

Bertrand Lens
Sometimes called Amici-Bertrand lens. A lens placed in the tube of a petrographic microscope above the analyzer. This lens when used in combination with the eyepiece of the microscope acts as an objective to view interference figures under conoscopic examinations.

Biaxial
Having two optical axes.

Binocular Body
See Eyepiece, Binocular.

Binocular Microscope
A microscope having a binocular body with two eyepieces so that both eyes may be used.

Binocular Vision
The observation of an object or image by both eyes giving true three dimensional effects.

Biot Compensator
  See Compensator
Birefringence
  A property possessed by many crystals of having more than one refractive index. This depends on how the light passes through the crystal.
Brownian Movement
  A vibration of colloidal particles when they are suspended in a fluid.
Bulls Eye Condenser
  A fairly large lens used for concentrating a beam of light directed in the direction of an object or mirror.

C

Camera Lucida
  A device used with a microscope in order to see at the same time the image of the object and that of a pencil and paper which are placed on the table next to the microscope. Used for drawing.
Cap Analyzer
  An Analyzer placed above the eyepiece of a microscope instead of being between the objective and the eyepiece.
Cardioid Condenser
  See Condenser, dark field.
Cell, (Apparatus)
  A container made of transparent material for holding liquids through which light must pass.
Cell, Filter
  A cell which contains a colored liquid solution thus functioning as a light filter.
Chromatic Aberration
  See Aberration.
Chromatism
  Color fringes around an image due to chromatic aberration.
Coma
  When the sine law has not been followed in the design of an objective the image which it forms is fuzzy. It is then said that such an objective has coma.
Comparison Eyepiece
  See Eyepiece.
Compensator
  An optical device for determining the retardation or bire-

fringence of crystals. Among them are the selenite and mica plates, quartz wedge, Berek compensator, Babinet compensator, Biot compensator and others. They are generally used with polarizing microscopes.

Compensating Eyepiece
See Eyepiece.

Compound Microscope
A microscope which has an objective and an eyepiece. It gives an inverted image of the object.

Concavo-Convex
A lens which has a concave surface of a greater radius of curvature than that of its convex surface.

Condenser (substage)
A lens or a combination of lenses used in the substage of a microscope to illuminate the object under observation.

Condenser, Abbe
The substage condenser developed by Abbe which when properly used gives a numerical aperture of 1.20.* It is usually composed of two lenses. The three lens Abbe condenser gives an N.A. of 1.40.

Condenser Achromatic
A substage condenser which has been corrected for chromatic aberration. It is usually corrected also for spherical aberration.

Condenser Aplanatic
A substage condenser corrected for spherical aberration, but not necessarily for chromatic aberration.

Condenser, Dark Field
A condenser designed to illuminate an object so that it will be seen bright on a dark background. There are several types such as the parabaloid and cardioid. The parabaloid is easier to use but the cardioid gives a more precise point illumination. Another very popular type is the "bispheric" which is similar to the cardioid.

Condenser, Spectacle Lens
A simple single lens condenser sometimes used to illuminate an object being observed with very low power objectives.

Conical Illumination
Employed with some vertical illuminators to illuminate opaque material. The central rays are eliminated so that the object is lighted by a hollow cone of light.

* Modern Abbe condensers give an N.A. of 1.25.

Conoscopic Observation

The observation of the interference figure of a crystal which is formed on the back lens of an objective when the crystal is placed between crossed prisms and illuminated by converging rays of light.

Converging Rays

Rays which are traveling forward together in such a manner that they will eventually meet.

Convexo-Concave

A lens which has one convex surface of a greater radius of curvature than that of its concave surface.

Counting Chamber

Heavy glass slides in which a cell has been ground. The cell has an exact depth so that when covered with an optically flat cover glass the volume of the cell per unit area is accurately known. On the floor of the cell fine lines are drawn in convenient patterns so that particles in suspension are seen over the ruled area. A count can thus be made on the volume basis.

Cover Glass

A very thin piece of glass which may be round, square or rectangular which is used for covering a prepared object on a microscope slide. If possible it should be approximately .18mm thick.

Cover Glass Micrometer

A mechanical device used for measuring the thickness of a cover glass. It is accurate to hundredths of a mm.

Critical Angle

The angle which represents the dividing line between those light rays which just can emerge from a medium to pass into another less dense parallel to the surface from which they emerge; and those rays starting from the same source which just cannot emerge from the denser medium and therefore must be reflected back into it.

Critical Illumination

The illumination of an object in such a manner that the condenser forms an image of the source of the light on the plane of the object at the same time filling the back lens of the objective with light but not with more light than is exactly necessary to fill it.

Crossed Prisms (Crossed Nicols)

That position of the analyzer and polarizer of a polarizing

microscope wherein no light reaches the eye unless an optically active object is placed between the prisms. In a microscope the object would be under the objective.

Cross Line Eyepiece
See Eyepiece.

Crystallographic Axis
The directions in a crystal by means of which some of its characteristics are determined.

Curvature of Field
An image of an object formed by a lens is not on a perfectly flat plane. This is the reason why the image formed by a microscope objective is not in perfect focus throughout the entire field of view. Curvature of field is proportionately more apparent as the magnification of an objective increases.

D

Dark Field Condenser
See Condenser.

Dark Field Illumination
That type of illumination which shows the object bright on a dark background. The dark field condenser is generally used for this purpose. Also whenever light rays strike the object sufficiently obliquely to prevent their entering the objective.

Demonstration Ocular (or Eyepiece)
See Eyepiece.

Depth of Focus
See Focus.

Diameters
The term used to express the rate of linear magnification of an object.

Diaphragm
A device to reduce or control the aperture of a lens or the diameter of a beam of light.

Diaphragm Davis
An iris diaphragm so mounted that it can be used between the objective and the tube of the microscope.

Diaphragm Iris
An adjustable diaphragm consisting of several movable leaves which close or open symmetrically to form an opening of variable diameter. Used in condensers, objectives, camera lenses, etc.

Diaphragm, Stop

1. A diaphragm with the central portion opaque so light can go through only *around* the central portion, i.e., dark field wheel diaphragm.

2. A diaphragm which has a fixed opening.

Diaphragm Slit

A diaphragm wherein the opening is a narrow slit.

Diatom

An unicellular alga surrounded by a wall of silica which has extremely fine markings and or perforations. Often used to test the resolving qualities of microscope objectives. There are many thousand species of diatoms.

Dicroscopic Eyepiece

See Eyepiece.

Diffraction

A deviation of rays of light from a straight course when partially cut off by any obstacle, or when passing near the edges of an opening.

Dispersion

The separating of the various wave lengths of light which compose white light when it is refracted. This happens when light passes through a prism or a lens.

Diverging Rays

Rays of light traveling forward together but drawing away from each other so that they will never meet.

Double Concave

A lens which has two concave surfaces.

Double Convex

A lens which has two convex surfaces.

Drawing Eyepiece

See Eyepiece.

E

Eikonometer

An accessory for making measurements with the microscope. Fits over the eyepiece of the microscope and has a scale so that the image can be seen superimposed on the scale.

Emergent Rays

Rays of light coming from a refracting surface.

Empty Magnification

A magnification greater than that where the maximum resolution is possible.

Equivalent Focus

The focus of a single theoretical lens which has the same power and the same characteristics than the combination of lenses composing the lens considered.

Erect Image

See Image.

Extinction Angle

The angle through which an optically active object must be rotated between crossed polarizing prisms (or equivalent) from a position parallel to the cross hairs of the eyepiece to the position where it disappears. Usually measured with the graduation of the rotating circular stage of a polarizing microscope.

Eyepiece

The lens or combination of lenses used in the upper end of a microscope tube. The second magnifying element of a compound microscope.

Eyepiece, Binocular (Binocular Body)

A device which divides a beam of light into two different beams and directs them through two eyepiece tubes so that both eyes can be used at the microscope. Generally used in place of, or on top of, the tube of the microscope.

Eyepiece Comparison

A device which is placed over the eyepieces of two different microscopes to bring together in one field, side by side, the images coming from each microscope.

Eyepiece Compensating

A specially designed eyepiece for use especially with apochromatic objectives to compensate for certain inherent defects of such lenses. Usually the lower power compensating oculars are of the huyghenian type of design, and the higher powers: i.e., 15x, 20x, etc., of the Ramsden type. (See Oculars and Apochromatic objectives Chapter II.)

Eyepiece, Cross Line or Cross Hair

An eyepiece provided with cross hair lines which can be seen superimposed on the image of the object. Generally used with polarizing microscopes.

Eyepiece, Demonstration

A device having two eyepieces, one over the tube of the microscope and the other at the end of a side tube. Used to enable two people to view at the same time the image shown by one microscope.

Eyepiece Dicroscopic

A special eyepiece which has a rectangular diaphragm equipped with a calcite prism to examine simultaneously side by side the two images formed by the ordinary and extraordinary rays.

Eyepiece, Drawing

An eyepiece equipped with a prism used to project the image onto a piece of paper for drawing. Some are so constructed that they can be used as a camera lucida if the microscope is inclined about 30 to 45 degrees.

Eyepiece, Filar Micrometer

See Filar Micrometer.

Eyepiece, Flat Field

Eyepieces specially designed to give a flatter field than the huyghenian or compensating. Sold under different trade names by the various manufacturers, i.e., Hyperplane (B & L), Orthoscopic (Zeiss), etc.

Eyepiece Huyghenian

The usual type of microscope eyepiece composed of two plano convex lenses with a diaphragm between them. The convex surfaces of both lenses face downward. It is a negative combination.

Eyepiece Micrometer

A huyghenian eyepiece with a graduated scale in the plane of the diaphragm. Has a focusable eye lens. Used for measurements after it has been calibrated.

Eyepiece Projection

An eyepiece of low magnification and long focus used for projection. Has a focusable eye lens to accommodate for projection distance.

Eyepiece, Ramsden

A positive combination composed of two plano convex lenses (which together act as a single magnifier), with the convex surfaces facing each other. The diaphragm is below the lower lens. Generally used for the higher magnifications of compensating Eyepieces.

Eyepiece, Screw Micrometer

See Screw Micrometer.

Eyepiece, Wright's

An eyepiece with a slot to receive compensators for work with a polarizing microscope. Used with a cap anaylzer.

Eye Point

The place above the top lens of an eyepiece where the eye must be placed so that the entire field of view can be seen. This is the point where the light rays coming from the ocular cross and become diverging instead of converging. Sometimes called *Ramsden Circle*. This point is not a perfect point but rather a small circle.

Eye Shield

An accessory which can be attached to the tube of the microscope so that if the unused eye remains open it will be shielded from extraneous light. These shields have also been made to fit binocular microscopes to prevent extraneous light from reaching the oculars.

F

Filar Micrometer

An eyepiece, usually of the Ramsden type which has a scale in the plane of focus. Over this scale is a movable cross hair actuated by a graduated drum which permits the exact measurement of very small objects. Must be calibrated with a stage micrometer before measurements are possible.

Field

The circular portion of an object which can be seen or projected with a given combination of objective and eye-piece.

Filter (Light)

A transparent substance or medium placed between the light source and the condenser of a microscope. It may be colored glass or gelatine film, colored liquid, clear liquid (like plain water), or neutral tint glass. Used for eliminating certain wave lengths of light, to cool the light or to transmit only a certain percentage of light from a given source.

Fine Adjustment

See Adjustment, Fine.

Fluorite Objective

See Objective Fluorite.

Focal Plane

The plane at the focal point which is at right angles to the optic axis.

Focus

This must be divided into two designations: 1. The position where light rays coming from an object placed on one side of a lens are brought together on the other side to form an image of the object. 2. The distance from the above mentioned focal position to the lens.

Focus, Conjugate

The focal point of an image (or the focal distance) which corresponds to any given object distance.

Focus, Depth of

The extent at which an object can be seen fairly distinctly above and below the theoretical focal plane of a given lens.

Focus Equivalent

See Equivalent Focus.

Focus, Principal

The focal distance of the image of an object when the object is located at infinity, i.e., the object may be the sun. Generally implied when simply "focus" is used, i.e., "This lens has a 10 inch focus."

Foot (of a microscope)

The base of the microscope, i.e., the horseshoe base.

Frequency of Light

The number of vibrations of light of a given wave length occurring per second.

F—Ratio or Value

Generally used to designate the "speed" or light transmitting properties of photographic lenses. The F value is the rated focus of a lens divided by its effective diameter, i.e., a 6 inch focus lens with an effective diameter of 2 inches would have a value of F 3.00. The lesser the F number the faster the lens, i.e., and F 3 lens is faster than an F 4 lens, etc.

G

Glycerine Immersion Objective

An immersion objective designed for use with glycerine as the immersion medium.

Greenough Binocular

See Stereoscopic Microscope.

Gypsum Plate

See Selenite Plate.

H

High Aperture

A term used to designate objectives which have a Numerical Aperture higher than 1.00. Also to condensers having an N.A. greater than 1.25.

Homogeneous Immersion
  See Objective, Immersion.
Huyghenian Eyepiece
  See Eyepiece, Huyghenian.

I

Illumination, Conical
  See Conical Illumination.
Illumination, Critical
  See Critical Illumination.
Illumination, Dark Field
  See Dark Field Illumination.
Illumination Köhler
  See Köhler Illumination.
Illumination, Opaque
  See Top Illumination.
Illumination Transparent
  See Transparent Illumination.
Illuminator, Lieberkuhn
  See Lieberkuhn Illuminator.
Illuminator, Silverman
  See Silverman Illuminator.
Illuminator, Vertical
  See Vertical Illuminator.
Image
  A "reproduction" formed by a lens of an object. It may appear larger or smaller than the object depending on the lens.
Image Distance
  The distance from the image plane to the optical center of a lens.
Image, Erect
  An image which is right side up. It looks the same as the object and not upside down.
Image, Inverted
  An image which is upside down. The lower part of the object would be the top of the image and vice versa. It is also transposed with respect to the object as regards the right and left sides.
Image, Real
  That type of image formed by a lens which can be projected or photographed.
Image, Virtual
  That type of image which can be seen only with the eye.

It does not actually exist in space. The image seen in a mirror is a good example.

Immersion Objective
   See Objective, Immersion.

Incident Rays
   Rays of light proceeding toward a surface.

Inclination Joint
   The hinged point of a microscope which permits the inclination of the instrument exclusive of the base.

Infra Red
   See Spectrum.

Interference Colors
   The colors which can be seen in optically active materials when such materials are placed between polarizing prisms.

Interference Figure
   The figure which can be seen on the back lens of an objective when optically active materials are examined conoscopically.

Inverted Image
   See Image, Inverted.

K

Köhler Illumination
   That type of illumination wherein the microscope condenser forms an image of the light source near the back lens of the objective or near its optical center. Now almost universally used for photomicrography.

L

Lamp (Microscope)
   The lamps which are used to illuminate specimens for observations with the microscope.

Lens
   A disc of glass or other transparent material which has been worked to accurate spherical surfaces (at least one) so that when light rays pass through it they change their direction according to the law of refraction.

Lens, Negative
   A lens which has one or both surfaces concave. It is called negative because it cannot form a "real" image by itself and it neutralizes the effect of a positive lens of identical focus. A huyghenian ocular is a negative *combination* and that is why

it cannot be used as a hand magnifier unless it is turned upside down.

Lens, Positive

A lens which has one or both surfaces convex. It can produce a "real" image—The Ramsden Ocular is a positive *combination* and hence can be used as a hand magnifier.

Lieberkuhn Illuminator

Consists of a concave mirror surrounding the objective to reflect light coming from below onto an opaque object placed under the objective. Used very seldom now.

Light (as concerns the microscope)

Energy transmitting vibrations of such a wave length that they may be apparent to the human eye. White light is composed of many wave lengths. The eye is sensitive only to those between about .4 to .7 microns. Those invisible rays of a longer wave length are called *Infra Red* radiations and those shorter than .4 microns are called *Ultra Violet* radiations.

Light Axial

Light traveling in a direction parallel to the optic axis.

Light Oblique

Light which strikes an object at an angle to the optic axis.

Light Polarized

Light which has been forced to vibrate in only one direction perpendicular to its forward motion instead of in all possible directions.

Light, Monochromatic

Light which has only one wave length as distinguished from that of several wave lengths. This term is also often used to describe light of a very narrow band of frequencies so that it is almost truly monochromatic.

Loup

A magnifying glass of low magnification. Usually less than 6x.

M

Macrograph

See Photomacrograph.

Magnification

The rate of enlargement of an object from which a real or virtual image is formed. The rates of comparative magnifications seen by the eye in the microscope are the ratio of the apparent size of the object to the size of the object as it appears to the unaided eye at a distance of 10 inches. If an object which at 10 inches appears to the unaided eye as 1mm is then viewed through the microscope and it then appears as 6mm, then the magnification is 6x. Usually expressed in *diameters*. The magnification of the area would then be the square of the diameters.

Magnified

Which appears larger than it really is because of the formation of a real or virtual image.

Magnifier

A magnifying glass of higher power than a loup, usually between 6x and 24x. Sometimes, however, the large diameter reading glasses which give a magnification of 1.5x to 2.5x are also called *magnifiers*.

Mechanical Stage

See Stage, Mechanical.

Mechanical Tube Length

See Tube Length.

Meniscus Lens

A lens which has one concave surface and one convex. This means that concavo-convex and convexo-concave lenses are meniscus lenses.

Metallurgical Microscope

A microscope especially designed for the observation of metal objects.

Mica Plate

A compensator for use with the polarizing microscope to determine the optic sign of a crystal. They are available in various retardation thicknesses.

Micrograph

See Photomicrograph.

Micromanipulator

An ingenious device for performing dissections and operations on an object under high magnifications. It is possible to operate on very minute objects with the aid of this instrument. Is is really a microscope accessory.

Micrometer

A device for making accurate small measurements. See Filar and Screw Micrometers, Eyepiece Micrometer, Stage Micrometer and Cover Glass Micrometer.

Micron

The 1/1000 of a millimeter. It is 1/25,400 of an inch. The unit of measurement for microscopic objects.

Microphotograph

This term is often used erroneously in place of Photomicrograph. Microphotograph means a very small photograph of a fairly large object which has been *reduced* so that this photograph can be observed under a microscope.

Microtome

An instrument for cutting thin sections of materials too large or not sufficiently transparent for direct examination with the microscope.

Millimeter

The 1/1000 part of a meter. About 1/25 of an inch.

Minified

The exact opposite of magnified—appearing smaller than its real size.

Mirror

The reflecting surface used under the stage of the microscope to direct the light toward the object or substage condenser. It usually has a plane surface and a concave surface.

Mirror Arm

The bar which supports the microscope mirror.

Monochromatic Light

See Light, Monochromatic.

Monochromatic Objective

An objective which has been designed to work only with a predetermined wave length of light.

Monochromator

A special illuminating device which permits the use of any band of color for illuminating a microscopic object. It separates white light into its component wave lengths.

Monocular

Generally used to distinguish a microscope with one ocular tube from a *binocular* which has two ocular tubes. The conventional microscope therefore is a monocular compound microscope.

N

N.A.

See Numerical Aperture.

Negative Lens

See Lens, Negative.

Newton's Scale

The series of interference colors arranged according to their

Order, i.e., I, II, III, IV. The colors run through violet to red and then start over again, hence the *Order*.

Nicol Prism

The original form of polarizing prism. Often used to indicate any polarizing prism, although there are other forms such as the Ahrens and the Glan-Thompson which are now in use more than the Nicol type.

Nosepiece, Revolving

A device for the rapid changing of the working position of objectives. A rotating disc receives two, three or four objectives so that any one of them may be rotated quickly into the optical axis of the microscope.

Numerical Aperture (N.A.)

The term suggested by Abbe to express the ability of a lens to resolve fine details in an object as well as its light gathering capacity in comparison with another lens. This value is obtained by multiplying the sine of one half of its angular aperture by the index of refraction of the medium between the objective lens and the object. Formula is *n sine u.* N is the refractive index of the medium and u is half of the angular aperture.

O

Object (microscopic)

A specimen prepared for examination under the microscope.

Object, Opaque

An object which does not permit the light to go through it. Must be illuminated with reflected light.

Object, Test

A specimen used to test the performance of objectives.

Object, Transparent

An object which permits the light to go through it so that it can be examined with transmitted light.

Objective Changer

A device designed to make possible the rapid change of objectives from and to their working position. The revolving nosepiece is a good example. There are others such as the drum nosepiece and the sliding changer for stereoscopic microscopes.

Object Distance

The distance from the optical center of a lens to an object.

Object Marker

An accessory used for marking for future reference a particular point on a microscope slide.

Object Plane

The plane perpendicular to the axis of a lens which passes through the conjugate focus on which the object is located.

Objective

The lens in a microscope which is nearest to the object and which acts as the first magnifying element of the instrument.

Objective, Achromatic

An objective corrected against chromatic aberration for two colors and against spherical aberration for one color;

Objective, Apochromatic

An objective corrected against chromatic aberration for three colors and against spherical aberration for two colors.

Objective Dry

An objective designed to be used with air as the *only* medium between it and the cover glass (or object).

Objective, Fluorite

An objective with better corrections than the achromatic (which is possible by the use of the mineral "fluorite" in its construction). Not as good as the apochromatic however. Sometimes called semi-apochromatic.

Objective, Immersion

An objective designed to be used with a liquid medium between its front lens and the object (or cover glass). The medium for which the objective is designed must be used with it, i.e., cedar oil, glycerine, water, etc.

Oblique Light

See Light, Oblique.

Oblique Rays

Rays of light which travel at an appreciable angle to the optic axis.

Ocular

A synonym for Eyepiece. See Eyepieces.

Oil Immersion Objective

An immersion objective designed to be used with cedar oil. (Refractive index 1.515.)

Opaque Illumination

See Top Illumination.

Optic Axis

A line passing through the exact center of a lens (through the curved surfaces).

Optic Axis (in Crystallography)
In uniaxial crystals—The single axis of optical symmetry.
In biaxial crystals—One of their two axes.

Optical Center
That point on the lens axis through which pass all the rays without suffering any angular deviation.

Optical Tube Length
See Tube Length.

Orthoscopic
Giving a true image. Sometimes used as a trade name for lenses.

Over-correction
More than the proper correction against some inherent defect of lenses. The opposite of Under-correction.

P

Parabaloid Condenser
See Condenser, Darkfield.

Parallel Rays
See Rays.

Parfocal
Adjusted or constructed to focus at the same point.

Petrographic Microscope
An advanced type of polarizing microscope designed for the examination of materials illuminated with polarized light. It differs from the simpler polarizing microscope in that it has a Bertrand Lens for observation of interference figures and in that the analyzer is located in the tube of the microscope between the Bertrand Lens and the objective.

Photomacrograph
A photograph of an object enlarged only a few diameters, usually not exceeding 10 or 15.

Photomicrograph
A photograph taken with a microscope. Usually taken at a fairly high or very high magnification.

Pillar
That part of the base of the microscope which extends from the horse shoe base to the inclination joint.

Pinion
See Rack and Pinion.

Plano-Concave
A lens which has one flat surface and the other concave.

Plano-Convex
A lens which has one flat surface and the other convex.

Polarized Light
See Light, Polarized.

Polarizer
The polarizing device (prism or otherwise) generally used below the stage of the microscope for the initial polarization of ordinary light. (Some of the modern vertical illuminators can be equipped with a polarizing prism which is also correctly called a polarizer). See also Analyzer.

Polarizing Microscope
A microscope equipped with a polarizer and analyzer and preferably with a circular, rotating, graduated stage. Designed for the study of specimens illuminated with polarized light. The petrographic microscope is a more complete type of polarizing microscope.

Polarizing Object
An object which shows the colors and effect upon it of polarized light.

Polarizing Prism
A compound prism (generally of calcite) which has been so cut and cemented that it will polarize light. The usual types are the Glan-Thompson, Ahrens and Nicol.

Polaroid (Trade Name)
A material in sheet form which has the property of polarizing light.

Power
This term is commonly used synonymously with magnification, i.e. high or low power, meaning high or low magnification.

Principal Focus
See Focus, Principal.

Prism
An optical device made of a transparent material like glass which will change the direction of a ray of light according to the law of refraction.

Q

Quarter Wave Plate
A compensator used with polarizing microscopes. A thin disc of mica of such a thickness that it will retard the slow ray one quarter of a wave length.

Quartz Cell or Chamber
A transparent shallow quartz receptacle used for studying colloidal fluids illuminated on a dark field.

Quartz Condenser
A substage condenser made of quartz instead of glass. It is used for ultra-violet work with the microscope.

Quartz Optics
Lenses of a microscope such as condensers, objectives and eyepieces which are made of quartz instead of glass to allow the passage through them of ultra-violet light. Used in special photomicrographic work.

Quartz Wedge
A compensator used with polarizing microscopes. See Compensator.

Quick Screw Substage
A vertical screw which was formerly used to move the substage condenser of a microscope up and down. Now obsolete. The rack and pinion is used in modern microscopes for this purpose.

R

Rack and Pinion
A combination of a pinion and a diagonally cut rack which makes it possible to move up and down very smoothly the tube or the condenser of a microscope.

Ramsden Eyepiece (or ocular)
See Eyepiece, Ramsden.

Ramsden Circle
See Eye Point.

Ray (of Light)
An imaginary line of light. An enormous number of rays constitute a beam of light.

Rays, Converging
Light rays traveling forward together toward each other so that they will eventually meet.

Rays, Diverging
Rays of light traveling forward together but drawing away from each other so that they will never meet.

Rays, Parallel
Rays of light traveling forward together parallel to each other so that they will never meet nor separate.

Real Image
See Image.

Reducing Glass

A negative lens, concave, which reduces the size of an object instead of magnifying it.

Refraction

The bending of light rays as they pass *at an oblique angle* from one medium to another more or less dense, i.e., from air to glass, from glass to air, etc.

Refraction, Law of

When refraction occurs, the light rays bend *toward* the perpendicular if they pass into a denser medium (air to water), and *away from* the perpendicular if they pass into a less dense medium (water to air).

Refractive Index

The measure of the refraction of a light ray as it passes at an oblique angle from one medium to another more or less dense. The index of air is taken as 1.00 and all the other mediums have a higher index, i.e., water 1.336; ordinary glass about 1.50; Canada Balsam 1.544 and Quartz 1.547. The refractive index is usually measured with an instrument called the *Refractometer*.

Resolution

The ability of a certain objective to resolve or break up an object into its component details so that they may be seen. This is a function of the wave length of light and the N.A. of the objective used. See Resolution, Limit of.

Resolution, Limit of

A measure of the maximum capacity of a lens to resolve details. Since resolution is taken as the shortest distance at which a lens will show two points as *two* instead of as one fuzzy point, its limit of resolution would be "y" (the wave length of light used) divided by "N.A." (its numerical aperture). Thus the formula is (taking R for resolution) $R = Y/N.A.$ If a condenser is used, it is $R = Y/2N.A.$

Rheinberg Illumination

A form of illumination used with transparent objects which is accomplished by the use of certain colored discs placed below the condenser. The use of these discs in the condenser make the object appear of a contrasting color to the field.

S

Screen

A reflecting surface on which an image is projected. Sometimes this term is also used as a synonym for "filter."

Screw Micrometer Eyepiece

An Eyepiece, usually of the Ramsden type, which has a movable scale in the plane of focus so that it can be seen superimposed on an object. The scale is movable by a micrometer screw actuated by a graduated drum so that very fine measurements can be made after calibration of the scale. Similar to, but different from, the Filar Micrometer.

Selenite Plate

A compensator used with polarizing microscopes. Available in the red-violet of the various orders. Sometimes called Gypsum Plate.

Semi-Apochromatic

A term often used to describe Fluorite Objectives.

Silverman Illuminator

An anular lamp (ring of light) placed *around* an objective to illuminate opaque objects. Very popular at one time.

Simple Microscope

A microscope having only one magnifying element instead of two like in the compound microscope. A magnifier held by the hand and used to magnify an object becomes a simple microscope.

Slide

1. A glass slip used to receive microscopic specimens.
2. A prepared specimen mounted on a slide.

They are usually 3 x 1 or 3 x 2 inches.

Slit Ultra Microscope

See Ultra Microscope.

Solar Focus

See Focus, Principal

Spectrum

Light which has passed through a prism (or diffracted with a grating) and separated into its various component colors. The visible spectrum runs from violet to indigo to blue to green to yellow to orange and to red. Light of such short or long wave lengths that it is not visible is called ultra-violet or infra-red respectively.

Stage

The platform of a microscope on which the object is placed for observation.

Stage Adjustable

A stage which can be moved up and down. This term should not be confused with "mechanical stage."

Stage Mechanical

a—A stage so constructed that it can be moved in two or three directions by some mechanical means and thus the object can be moved slowly and with perfect control to the desired position.

b—An accessory placed on the stage of the microscope which permits the movement of an object in two directions for the same purpose as above.

Stage, Rotating Universal

An accessory developed for use with petrographic microscopes. With it, it is possible to rotate and incline a specimen to any angle or position.

Stage Micrometer

A fine exact scale engraved or photographed on a slide and then (if on a transparent slide) protected with a cover glass. Usually the scale is 2 millimeters divided to 0.01mm. If engraved on metal it is often in inches, that is, a 0.2″ scale ruled to 0.001″.

Stand

The complete assembly of mechanical parts of the microscope without optical parts but generally including the mirror.

Stereoscopic Microscope

A microscope composed of two different compound microscopes built together at an angle from each other, each having prisms between the objectives and eyepieces, which erect the image of the object so that it can be seen right side up instead of inverted. With this microscope it is possible to see the depth (third dimension) of an object. Often called Greenough Binoculars, Greenough microscopes or just "Greenoughs."

Stop

A diaphragm for reducing the aperture of a lens or to block out its central portion, i.e., funnel stop for objectives; dark field stop for condensers; field stop for microscope lamps.

Sub-Microscopic

So small that they cannot be seen with a microscope.

Substage

The mechanical and optical parts located *under* the stage of the microscope.

T

Test Object
    See Object, Test.
Test Plate, Abbe
    A special test object consisting of parallel lines cut on a metal surface deposited on a transparent slide. The lines are covered with a thin wedge of glass so that it is possible to see the lines under various cover glass thicknesses. Used for testing the performance of objectives for color, cover glass correction, definition, etc.
Test Plate, Ruled Gratings
    A transparent test plate on which lines have been cut with a diamond at successively closer intervals. It is used for testing the resolution of objectives. Very fine rulings have been made going up to 120,000 lines per inch.
Top Illumination
    The illumination of an object from *above* the stage, either directly down like in a vertical illuminator or at an angle.
Transparent Illumination
    The illumination of an object which is sufficiently transparent to permit light to pass *through it* to the objective. This light comes from below the stage, either directly from the mirror or from the substage condenser.
Transmitted Light
    See Transparent Illumination.
Tube
    That part of the microscope which receives the objective at one end and the eyepiece at the other.
Tube Length, Mechanical
    The distance from the top of the tube which receives the eyepiece to the shoulder against which rests the objective when it is screwed in position. This distance includes the dimension of the nosepiece, or if there is no nosepiece, the adapter which takes its place. Usually 160 or 170mm.
Tube Length, Optical
    The distance from the front focal plane of the eyepiece to the rear focal plane of the objective.

U

Ultra-Microscope
    The term used to describe the combination of a microscope,

necessary condensers, slit and lamp by means of which colloidal particles are sometimes observed on a dark field. A powerful beam of light is sent through a slit at a right angle to the axis of a high power objective, thus illuminating the particles on a dark field. A dark field condenser also gives a similar effect.

Ultra-Microscopic
Objects or particles so small that they can be seen only with the aid of the Ultra-Microscope, or perhaps a dark field condenser.

Ultra-Violet Light
Those light waves of a shorter wave length and greater frequency than the violet waves of the visible spectrum.

Ultra-Violet Microscope
A microscope having all its optics made of some material which will allow the passage of ultra violet light. Quartz is generally used for this purpose. The term usually includes the *source* of ultra-violet light.

Under-Correction
Not enough correction against spherical and chromatic aberrations. The opposite of over correction.

Uniaxial
A type of crystal which has only one optical axis.

Universal Rotating Stage
See Stage, Rotating Universal.

V

Vernier
A secondary graduation used to divide into smaller parts the main graduation which slides next to it. Usually it has ten parts in a space occupied by nine parts of the main scale thus subdividing one space of the primary scale into 10 parts. A vernier next to a graduated circle divides degrees into a definite number of minutes of arc.

Vertical Illuminator
An accessory used to send a beam of light down through the objective in order to illuminate an opaque object. There are several types of vertical illuminators.

Virtual Image
See Image, Virtual.

Visible Spectrum
See Spectrum.

W

Water Immersion Objective
   An immersion objective designed to be used with water between the front lens and the cover glass or object.
Wave
   A complete cycle in the undulatory movement of light.
Wave Length of Light
   The distance from the crest of one wave to the next. In *visible* light this varies from 0.4 microns or 4000 Angstroms to 0.7 microns or 7000 Angstroms.
Wheel Stop
   A form of stop with spokes extending from it to the supporting shoulder so that the central opaque stop is supported in its proper position as regards the lens with which it is used. A dark field stop for substage condensers is a good example.
Working Distance
   The free space between the lowest part of an objective and the cover glass of proper thickness when the objective is in focus.
Wright's Universal Eyepiece
   See Eyepiece, Wright's.

A SELECTED BIBLIOGRAPHY

Th references listed below give the more recent contributions and may serve as sources of more detailed information. Popular, non-technical and the older less available books are omitted.

I. *Microscopy*

ALLEN, R. M. The Microscope—1940—275 pp.

ARNULF, A. La Theorie de la Limite de Visibilité par le Microscope. Bull. Soc. Fr. Microsc. 1939, 8:63–95.

BECK, C. The Microscope, Theory and Practice. 1938, London. 264 pp. Detailed discussion of optics, resolution, illumination and special equipment. Illustrated with British instruments.

BELLING, J. The Use of the Microscope. 1930. New York. 315 pp. Practical suggestions for effective use of the microscope.

CARPENTER, W. B. The Microscope and Its Revelations. Rev. by W. H. Dallinger, London. 8th ed., 1901, 1181 pp.

CHAMOT, E. M. and C. W. MASON, Handbook of Chemical Microscopy. 2nd ed. I. 1938 XIII + 478 pp. II 1939, New York XI + 438 pp.

The first volume covers general principles and use of the different kinds of microscopes and should be read by all microscopists. The second volume gives methods for qualitative chemical microanalysis.

319

CLAY, R. S. & T. H. COURT. History of the Microscope. 1932. London. 266 pp.
GAGE, S. H. The Microscope. 1941. 17th ed. Ithaca. 617 pp. Probably the most complete American text on the subject.
MARSHALL, C. R. & H. D. GRIFFITH. An Introduction to the Theory and Use of the Microscope. 1928, London. 90 pp. A well illustrated, brief manual of the microscope.
METZNER, P., Das Mikroskop. (Zimmerman). 2nd ed. 1928, Leipsig. XI + 509 pp. Detailed discussion of optics and methods, well documented and serves as a key to the Continental literature.
ROGERS, A. F. and KERR, PAUL F. Optical Mineralogy.
SPITTA, E. J. Microscopy 1920, 3rd ed. London. 534 pp.
WINCHELL, A. N. Elements of Optical Mineralogy.

II. *Microscopical Technique. (Biological)*

BENSLEY, R. R., & S. H. BENSLEY. Handbook of Histological and Cytological Technique. 1938. Chicago. 167 pp.
CHAMBERLAIN, C. J. Methods in Plant Histology. 5th ed. 1932. Chicago. XI + 416 pp. An elementary manual for botanists.
CONN, H. J. The History of Staining. 1933, Geneva. 141 pp. The development of staining methods with some formulae and bibliographic references.
Biological Stains. 4th ed. 1940, Geneva. 308 pp. The fundamental reference book on stains and their use.
GALIGHER, A. E. Essentials of Practical Microtechnique. 1934. Berkeley. 288 pp. A moderate sized manual with emphasis on practical methods. The part on microtomy should be of special aid to beginners.
GATENBY, J. B. & T. S. PAINTER. The Microtomist's Vade Mecum (Bolles Lee). 10th ed. 1937, Philadelphia. XI + 784 pp. An encyclopedic reference work; where to find special methods.
GUYER, M. F., Animal Micrology. 4th ed. 1936, Chicago, XVI + 331 pp. One of the most useful books for the beginner with methods for animal tissues and lists of difficulties and how to overcome them.
JOHANSEN, D. A. Plant Microtechnique. 1940. New York. 523 pp.
LISON, L. Les Methodes de Reconstruction Graphic Micro-

scopique. Act. Sci. et Ind., 1937. No. 553. Paris. 45 pp. Review and methods for making three dimensional models from sections.

McCLUNG, C. E., Editor. Handbook of Microscopical Technique. 2nd ed. 1937, New York XVII + 716 pp. General and special methods by specialists in each field; a well documented reference book.

MERCK INDEX, THE. 5th ed. 1940. 1060 pp. Descriptions of chemicals and drugs, tests, killing and fixing fluids and staining solutions.

MOSSMAN, H. W. Dioxan Technique. Stain Technology. 1937, 12: 147–156.

RICHARDS, O. W. 1942. The Effective Use and Proper Care of the Microtome. 88 pp. Spencer Lens Co. Buffalo.

ROMEIS, B., Taschenbuch der mikroskopischen Technik, 13th ed. 1932, Munchen. XIII + 801 pp. A very complete reference book on the preparation of biological materials for examination with the microscope and key to the European literature.

SCHMIDT, W. J. Anleitung zu Polarizations mikroskopishen Untersuchungen für Biologen. 1924. Bonn. 64 pp.

III. *Microscopy, Industrial*

ALLEN, R. M. The Microscope in Elementary Cast Iron Metallurgy. Chicago. 1939. 143 pp.

CALKIN, J. B. Microscopy of Paper. Tappi. 1937. New York, N. Y. 47 pp.

EGBERG, B. & N. E. PROMISEL. The Value of the Microscope to the Electroplater. Metal Ind., 1939, 37:255.

GARNER, W. Industrial Microscopy. 1932. London. 389 pp.

HANUSEK, T. F., Trans. by A. L. Winton, The Microscopy of Technical Products. 1907, New York. 471 pp. General methods for the examination of foods and other technical materials.

LINSLEY, L. C., Industrial Microscopy. 1929. Richmond. 286 pp. Methods for microchemical identification, papers, pulps, starches and textiles. Well illustrated with drawings and photomicrographs.

MATTHEW, J. M., Textile Fibers. 1916, New York, 630 pp.

MUNOZ, F. J. & HOLMES, WM. O. The Microscope in Textile Analysis. Rayon Textile Monthly. Jan. & Feb. 1941. Practical Article for beginners.

PLITT, T. M. Microscopic Methods used in Identifying Commercial Fibers. Circ. Nat. Bu. Standards. C-423. 1939. 26 pp.

PRESTON, J. M. Modern Textile Microscopy. 1933. London XI + 315 pp.

RUBIN, M. M., & M. L. RUBIN, Spots and Specs in Paper. Paper Ind. and Paper World. 1939, 21:423–434. Well illustrated with some photomicrographs in color.

SCHWARTZ, E. R., Textiles and the Microscope. 1934. New York. XI + 329 pp.

SHORT, M. N., Microscopic determination of the ore minerals. U. S. Geol. Surv., 1940. Bull. No. 914. 314 pp.

WALLIS, T. E., Analytical Microscopy. 1923. London VIII + 149 pp. Out of print, but sometimes found in second hand stores. How to prepare materials for examination with the microscope—is illustrated. Well worth obtaining when possible.

IV. *Microscopy, Agricultural and Public Health*

BRYAN, C. S., G. J. TURNEY, W. K. FOX, L. H. BEGEMAN, X. A. MILES and J. S. BRYAN. The Microscope in the Production of High Quality Milk. Jour. Milk Tech. 1938, 1:26–34. (Practical methods, including charts of use in locating infection and contamination.)

FRY, W. H. Petrographic Methods for Soil Analyses. U. S. Dept. Agri. Tech. Bull. No. 344. 1933. 96 pp.

GREENFIELD, L. & J. J. BLOOMFIELD. The Impinger Dust Sampling Apparatus. U. S. Pub. Health Repts. 1932. 47: 654–675. (Dust Counting Technic.)

KUBIENA, W. L. Micropedology. 1938. Ames, Iowa. 243 pp. (Soil microscopy.)

Standard Methods for the Examination of Dairy Products. Am. Public Health Assoc. New York City. 1939. 190 pp.

WHIPPLE, G. C., Microscopy of Drinking Water. Ithaca, 1927. XIX + 586 pp.

V. *Criminology*

CASTELLANOS, I. Identification Problems; Criminal and Civil. Brooklyn, N. Y. 1939. 215 pp.

GONZALES, T. A., M. VANCE and M. HELPERN. Legal Medicine and Toxicology. New York. 1937 XI + 754 pp.

GUNTHER, J. D., and C. O. GUNTHER, Identification of Firearms. New York. 1935. XXVIII + 342 pp.

HATCHER, J. S. Textbook of Firearm Investigation, Identification and Evidence. Marion, N. C. 1935. XIII + 533 pp.

LUCAS, A. Forensic Chemistry and Scientific Criminal Investigation. New York. 1935. 376 pp.

VI. *Photomicrography*

ALLEN, R. M. Photomicrography. 1941. 364 pp.

BARNARD, J. E., & F. V. WELCH. Practical Photomicrography 3rd ed. 1936. London. 352 pp.

CLERC, L. P. Photography, Theory and Practice. 2nd ed. 590 pp.

HIND, H. L., & W. B. RANDLES, Handbook of Photomicrography. 1937. N. Y. City.

NEBLETTE, C. B. Photography—its Principles and Practice. 3rd ed. 1938. N. Y. C. 652 pp.

Photomicrography. Eastman Kodak Co. 13 ed. 1935. Rochester, N. Y. 122 pp. Useful volume.

SCHMIDT, L. Photomacrography. Jour. Biol. Photogr. Assoc. 1937, 6:47–61. (Methods for magnifications up to 50X.)

Symposium Number. Jour. Photomicrogr. Soc. London. 1931, 15:1–293.

VII. *Journals*

American Microscopical Society, Transactions.

Biological Photographic Society, Journal.

The Microscope and Entomological Monthly.

Photo Technique.

Quarterly Journal of the Microscopical Science.

Royal Microscopical Society, Journal.

Société Française de Microscopie, Bulletin de la.

Stain Technology.

Zeitschrift für wissenschaftliche Mikroskopie.

INDEX

325

INDEX OF ILLUSTRATIONS

The illustrations have been grouped alphabetically under the following headings:

A—Old Microscopes.
B—Modern Microscopes.
C—Accessories for Microscopes.
D—Microscope technique.
E—Use of and pertaining to Polarizing Microscopes.
F—Microtomes.
G—Accessories for the Microtome and their correct use.
H—Photomicrographs.